PHOTOCOPIABLE ACTIVITIES TO DEVELOP GRAPHICAL INTERPRETATION SKILLS

HANDLING SCIENCE DATA

YEAR 5
SCOTTISH PRIMARY 6

PETER HARWOOD AND JOYCE PORTER

Authors	Editor	Series designer	Cover illustration
Peter Harwood	Joel Lane	Anna Oliwa	Edward Eaves
Joyce Porter			
	Assistant editor	Designer	Illustrations
	David Sandford	Anna Oliwa	Sarah Warburton

Text © Peter Harwood and Joyce Porter 2002
© 2002 Scholastic Ltd

Designed using Adobe Pagemaker

Published by Scholastic Ltd,
Villiers House,
Clarendon Avenue,
Leamington Spa,
Warwickshire CV32 5PR

Printed by Bell & Bain Ltd, Glasgow

5 6 7 8 9 0   7 8 9 0 1

British Library Cataloguing-in-Publication Data
A catalogue record for this book is available from the British Library.

ISBN 0-590-53830-6
ISBN 978-0590-53830-5

Visit our website at www.scholastic.co.uk

Acknowledgements
The authors and publishers wish to thank:

AstraZeneca Science Teaching Trust for their funding and support of the research project on which the activities in this book are based (you can visit the AZSTT website at www.azteachscience.co.uk).

The children of Knowsley, Powys and Trafford LEAs for their help in testing these investigations in the classroom.

The National Curriculum for England 2000
© The Queens Printer and Controller of HMSO.
Reproduced under the terms of HMSO Guidance Note 8.

A Scheme of Work for Key Stages 1 and 2: Science
© Qualifications and Curriculum Authority.
Reproduced under the terms of HMSO Guidance Note 8.

CONTENTS

PAGE NO.	ACTIVITY TITLE	GRAPH TYPE	SCIENCE CURRICULUM REFERENCES		
			QCA UNIT	NATIONAL CURRICULUM	SCOTTISH 5–14 GUIDELINES
10	Heart rate after exercise	Table of data	5A	Sc1: 1a; Sc2: 2d	The processes of life – Level C
12	Pulse rate returning to normal	Line graph	5A	Sc2: 2d	The processes of life – Level C; Physical health – Level C
14	Foods to stay healthy	Bar graph	5A	Sc2: 2b	Physical health – Level C
16	Is smoking bad for health?	Bar graph	5A	Sc2: 2g	Physical health – Level D
18	Germinating seeds	Bar graph, notes	5B	Sc2: 3a, d	The processes of life – Level B
20	Pollination	Bar graph	5B	Sc2: 3d	The processes of life – Level D
22	Sycamore seeds	Line graph	5B	Sc2: 3d	The processes of life – Level D
24	A growing baby	Line graph	5B	Sc2: 2f	The processes of life – Levels B, D
26	Soaking wet	Bar graph	5C	Sc3: 1e	Materials from Earth – Level C
28	Helium balloons	Line graph	5C	Sc3: 1e; Sc4: 2b, e	Materials from Earth – Level C; Forces and their effects – Level E
30	Fizzy drinks can	Line graph	5C	Sc3: 1e, 3e	Materials from Earth – Level C
32	Evaporating liquids	Bar graph	5D	Sc3: 2a, b, d	Changing materials – Levels B, C
34	Does surface area affect evaporation?	Stick graph	5D	Sc3: 2b, d	Changing materials – Levels C, D
36	Does water evaporate faster in wider beakers?	Table of data	5D	Sc3: 2d	Changing materials – Levels C, D
38	Puddles	Line graph	5D	Sc3: 2b, d	Changing materials – Levels C, D
40	Making a cold drink	Line graph	5D	Sc3: 2a, b, c, d	Changing materials – Level C
42	Heating a kettle	Line graph	5D	Sc3: 2b, c, d	Changing materials – Level C
44	Noisy instruments	Table of data	5F	Sc4: 3e, f	Properties and uses of energy – Level C
46	Sound graphs	Line graph	5F	Sc4: 3e, f, g	Properties and uses of energy – Level C
48	Traffic lights	Line graph	5F	Sc4: 3f	Properties and uses of energy – Level D
50	Sundial investigation	Bar graph, line graph	5E	Sc4: 3b, 4b, c	Earth in space – Level B
52	Sunrise, sunset	Bar graph	5E	Sc4: 4b, c, d	Earth in space – Level E
54	Time zones	Bar graph	5E	Sc4: 4c	Earth in space – Level E
56	Planet data	Bar graph	5E	Sc4: 4a	Earth in space – Level C
58	Night and day	Line graph	5E	Sc4: 4c, d	Earth in space – Level B; Properties and uses of energy – Level B

INTRODUCTION

WHY HAVE BOOKS ABOUT HANDLING DATA FOR SCIENCE?

Children's education should provide them with skills that will benefit them for the years to come. Against this background, their ability to read and interpret information from graphs and charts is not only essential for science, but also for everyday life, where children are exposed to information on television, in newspapers and in magazines.

In the early days of the National Curriculum, the APU[1] examined graph work in school science. They found that children could successfully carry out many of the basic skills involved in drawing graphs and extracting information from graphs. However, most of the children failed to look for and describe patterns in their data, and did not understand the wider applications of graphs. The AKSIS project[2] revisited the use and application of graphs in school science. In their research, they found *'that over 75% of pupils' graphs were incorrectly constructed and most pupils regarded graphs as an end in themselves.'* One of the aims of the project was *'that Scientific Enquiry should develop pupils' understanding of the nature of scientific activity and the relation between data and scientific theories.'*

More recently, the OFSTED subject report on Primary Science (1999–2000) concluded that *'science skills, such as handling data, that draw upon and develop numeracy need to be improved systematically. Pupils are given sufficient opportunity to develop their science through practical activities. However their ability to interpret their results and say what they have found out is sometimes hampered by their lack of understanding of charts and graphs and lack of practice in recognising patterns in data. When they are encouraged to draw their own conclusions and are helped in this by discussion with the teacher, they show better understanding of the science and can apply it in different circumstances.'*

INTRODUCING CHILDREN TO DATA IN SCIENCE

This series of books is timely, then. They have been produced to help children develop their skills in handling data and its interpretation in science. However, these activities came about initially not from a response to OFSTED, but out of a need expressed by teachers. We have undertaken a four-year research programme, 'Developing Excellence in Primary Science', generously funded by the AstraZeneca Science Teaching Trust. This project has involved working with a wide variety of children and teachers. It was not simply an academic research project: it was soundly based in the classroom, with real teachers and real children in real teaching situations.

The research team comprised a group of experienced practitioners in class teaching, and in advisory and academic research, who have worked closely with teachers to address the difficulties of trying to teach science effectively. Working with primary children, alongside their teachers, clearly showed us that there was a need to develop children's data-handling skills in situations that the children were not familiar with. There is a strong tendency for primary children to learn science in a specific context, which can then make it difficult for them to apply their new knowledge to other situations. On seeing a data-handling exercise, children would often respond, 'I haven't done this' – referring to the context, which was not relevant to simply interpreting the data.

An analysis of children's performance in the Key Stage 2 National Tests[3] concurs with the OFSTED report. It shows clearly that children experience considerable difficulty in applying their knowledge to new situations (a problem of contextualised learning) and in *describing* trends in an acceptable scientific format (although, on further questioning, the children showed an underlying ability to identify trends in data). In this series, both of these aspects of data–handling are addressed, and advice is given to help you develop these skills with your class.

The activities in *Handling Science Data* aim to highlight and provide opportunities to develop those skills that are common to data-handling, as well as showing the children activities that have a practical basis and are similar, but not necessarily identical, to some they have already done. This should help them to develop the confidence to tackle new scenarios and look primarily at the data itself.

The essential ability to analyse scientific evidence (as highlighted in the OFSTED reports) and to express these ideas scientifically has also been addressed. These are typically the '–er, –er' answers in National Test papers, for example: 'the larger the force, the bigger the stretch'. Examples that the children can practise with are given in several of the activities in this book. While children can often recognise a trend in data mentally, they find it difficult to express their ideas in a concise and complete way: a common response would be, for example, 'It gets bigger' (for an elastic material being stretched) – or the children may give very roundabout descriptions from which you might have to extract the trend. To overcome this difficulty, we have devised a writing structure involving a two-line jingle, rather like that of an old-fashioned train, into which the children can fit their response. In this example, the chant would be 'the bigger the force / the greater the stretch.' This focuses the children's ideas; they quickly get used to doing it and are pleased at being able to devise their own jingles. It provides a precise and concise format for expressing their ideas – but they still have to be able to identify the trend.

ABOUT THE *HANDLING SCIENCE DATA* SERIES
HOW THE BOOKS ARE ORGANISED

Each book in this series contains at least 25 activities, each comprising a page of teacher's notes and a photocopiable children's page. Some additional photocopiable resource pages are provided. Each activity provides data related to the curricula for life processes and living things, materials or physical processes, together with a set of questions that focus on interpreting the data.

The choice of science topics in this series has primarily been matched to the QCA's *Science Scheme of Work for Key Stage 2*, which many teachers in England are now using. However, the other UK curriculum documents have also been considered, and the teacher's notes give references for the National Curriculum in England, relevant units in the QCA's *Science Scheme of Work* and the Scottish *National Guidelines for Science 5–14*. It is intended that the activities can be used alongside any primary science scheme of work as reinforcement or revision.

The level of work has also been matched to the National Numeracy and Literacy Strategies, so that the work is set at an appropriate level, with suitable progression for the children in each year group.

FEATURES OF THE PHOTOCOPIABLES

The photocopiable worksheets in each book cater for a range of abilities in relation to graphical interpretation skills. On each sheet, the questions are generally arranged in order of increasing difficulty. Some are deliberately challenging to extend the most able children. The majority of the questions are simply about interpreting the data, so the children need not have done the investigation described in order to be able to answer the questions.

Some of the questions identify the key scientific ideas that are relevant to that investigation. It is hoped that the children will have internalised these key concepts if they have already explored the topic practically. Some questions are deliberately open-ended so they can be used as extension or research exercises, and provide ideal homework material. The questions cover a range of types and include:

- taking readings from graphs
- relating data to properties
- identifying and predicting trends
- investigative skills
- graph plotting and table design
- science understanding
- visualising an investigation.

The level of language varies between the different activities, and some children may need support with reading some of the worksheets. However, the topics do require technical vocabulary, so it is important that this is introduced and reinforced through any complementary lessons. One way to do this would be to let the children carry out the investigations themselves, and then to use these sheets to provide matching practice or revision material.

The system of notation used for the quoting of units in this series is *factor/ unit,* for example temperature/°C or mass/g. This is the accepted format at all levels of science (and recommended by the ASE), although brackets – temperature (°C) or mass (g) – are acceptable at school ages. It is good practice for children to learn to put units at the top of each column in a table when recording data. This is the mathematical justification for using the '/': everything in the column below is divided by the unit, hence */unit,* and only the numbers need to be written in the columns. Equally, when the children use spreadsheets, the software will not recognise a cell that contains both text and numbers, so the children need to remember only to use numbers.

FEATURES OF THE TEACHERS' NOTES

We feel strongly that the most valuable way to help the children engage with science is by carrying out activities that provide outcomes (which could be data or observations) around which a class discussion can take place. Almost all of the data presented here has come from actual children's work. These are tried and tested activities, although the nature of practical investigations means that they do not always work as successfully each time. All of the activities carry practical advice on how to carry out the activities that underpin the data. Some of these activities will be familiar to you, others not. Don't be afraid to try them out; the children will respond to them in a positive way, and the data is much more meaningful if it is 'real'.

Even the most experienced and qualified science teachers learn new things all the time; you cannot hope to remember everything you did at school or university (even if you went to all the lectures!). Very few primary teachers have the luxury of a post-16 science education, yet they are expected to be in a position to answer a wide range of children's questions. The teacher's notes provided with each activity give the answers to the questions on the worksheets (always useful!), together with the relevant background science associated with the activity. This is to assist you in dealing with questions that, in our experience, the enquiring minds of primary children might come up with, especially if your teaching is open-ended. These notes are not intended to state what you should teach the children about any topic, but to support your knowledge so that you can internalise the concepts and then deal more effectively with the children's ideas.

ABOUT *HANDLING SCIENCE DATA: YEAR 5*

The activities in this book largely follow the topics covered in Year 5 of the QCA's *Science Scheme of Work,* and are also aimed at Level C/D of the Scottish *National Guidelines for Science 5–14.* The majority of the graphs are either line graphs or bar graphs. A 'stick graph' is included, which can be used as an intermediate stage between bar graphs and line graphs.

USING COMPUTERS IN PRIMARY SCIENCE LESSONS

Children's confidence in using computers is increasing all the time. So is the availability of computers; most primary classrooms now contain one. Even so, most computer-based learning activities involve either using commercial software that provides children with interactive exercises or using the computer as a research tool. Many teachers are still not confident about using computers as an integral tool for learning science.

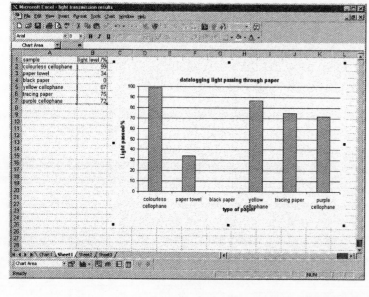

Nearly all of the activities in this series are derived from classroom investigations where, in addition to writing the results in an exercise book or a science folder, we have computerised data as a spreadsheet with a graph-plotting facility. The spreadsheet and graph can be used as a method of displaying and, more importantly, analysing the data. Information handling and working with spreadsheets (and databases) is developed throughout the QCA's *ICT Scheme of Work* in Key Stage 2. If the data is 'live' and on screen, children can predict the effect of changes in results on the appearance of the graph and check it instantaneously. If a result appears anomalous, the correct result can be predicted and inserted into the table and the effect observed immediately in the graph. This develops the skill of identifying trends in data – but at the same time demonstrates the value of careful measurement, which children at this age do not always readily appreciate. When they repeat the result, they will more often than not take more care – if necessary, you can intervene and discuss possible sources of error. This will develop the children's practical skills at the same time.

Each book in the series involves some examples of data collected by data-logging. This is a method of using electronic sensors to detect changes in light, temperature and sound, and then storing the data in a form that can be processed using appropriate computer software. This is specifically a feature of the QCA's *ICT Scheme of Work* in Years 5 and 6 (Units 5F and 6C).

Our research findings, reinforced by our own experiences, suggest that children are much better at interpreting graphs when the data is 'live' – for example, being plotted by the computer as the investigation is carried out.

USEFUL PRACTICAL TECHNIQUES

A 'germination sandwich' is a very good way of observing growing plants, because it is highly versatile. The balsa or square beading strips are glued on with bathroom sealant, but the Perspex cover is removable. The sandwich is filled with vermiculite (available from garden centres), which absorbs water but contains no nutrients that will interfere with the investigation. Two or three seeds can be planted near the top of the sandwich, which can then be stored (perhaps in a group of several sandwiches) in a container of water, so they are very economical for space. You can't over-water the plants, and if the container is kept topped up with water they will not dry out. The plants can be carefully teased out of the sandwich to allow the roots to be observed; then it can be replaced carefully as the investigation continues.

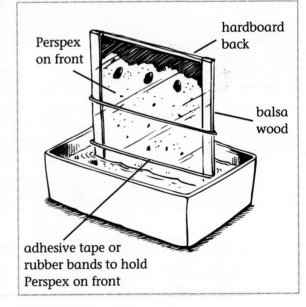

Many different factors can be investigated: seeds can be planted under different conditions (such as light, temperature, nutrients), or beans can be planted different ways up to see whether that makes a difference.

Photocopiable page 64 contains step-by-step instructions for planting seeds in a germination sandwich. The children can follow these when carrying out an investigation.

References
1. RM Taylor and P Swatton, *Assessment Matters No.1: Graph Work In School Science* (APU, 1991)
2. A Goldsworthy, R Watson and V Wood Robinson, *Getting to Grips with Graphs, Investigations, Developing Understanding* (ASE, 2000)
3. Standards at Key Stage 2 1996–2000 (QCA, 2001)

HEART RATE AFTER EXERCISE

> *National Curriculum Science* KS2 PoS Sc1: 1a; Sc2: 2d
> *QCA Science* Unit 5A: Keeping healthy
> *Scottish 5–14 Guidelines* The processes of life – Level C

HOW TO GATHER THE DATA

The Programme of Study for Sc1 (Scientific enquiry) in the English National Curriculum encourages the use of secondary sources of data. Research papers such as the one cited here (Stratton, G and Leonard, J 2002) are very useful for this purpose. You can use this example to encourage debate among the children about the benefits of exercise. If coloured lines were painted on the playground, would more of them exercise at breaktime? You may want to discuss what they think the researchers found out (in fact, the children's energy expenditure increased by 35%).

The children can predict what factors will change the pulse rate, and what types of exercise will raise it the most. The most difficult part of the investigation for the children is measuring their own pulse rates accurately. Hand-held pulse monitors are available from scientific suppliers for £17 each. If the children are taking their pulse by hand, remind them not to use the thumb because it has a pulse of its own. You can also ask the children:

■ why the research scientists took measurements from several boys and girls, not just one (for greater reliability of results)

■ why they measured the heart rate in the last minute of each activity (to make sure it had adjusted to the activity)

■ why they used special equipment to measure the heart rates (for greater accuracy).

The mean heart rate was measured using a short-range radio telemeter (Sport Tester from Polar-Electro Kemperle, Finland) strapped to each child's wrist, sending radio signals to a receiver that computerised the data.

THE SCIENCE BEHIND THE DATA

The heart is a pump made of powerful muscle. Each contraction of the heart's left ventricle sends a burst of oxygenated blood around the body, and we feel this as a pulse where an artery is close to the surface. The body's muscle cells use glucose and oxygen from the blood to release energy by respiration. When we exercise, the muscles need more energy (from the breakdown of glucose) and more oxygen, so the heart pumps faster to send more blood to the muscles. The body feels hot, because the muscles have been working harder than normal and more energy has been released. The breathing rate increases to supply more oxygen to the blood. During maximum effort, an adult heart pumps 34 litres of blood per minute.

Answers

1. 88 bpm

2. None (the boys were lying down).

3. Yes: not much energy is needed to lie still, so the heart rate should be low.

4. The girls' heart rate was higher than the boys' by 13 bpm.

5. 166 bpm

6. The girls had been running for 4 minutes, using up a lot of energy, so their hearts would have needed to beat very quickly.

7. 44 bpm

8. (You may need to discuss with groups how they can display two sets of data on one graph for comparison.)

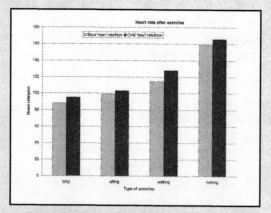

9. The children's heart rate was probably close to its maximum after 4 minutes of exercise, so it would not increase by much if the children exercised for a longer time.

10. The more active the exercise, the faster the heart rate (up to a maximum).

Heart rate after exercise

A team of research scientists were investigating whether a group of 27 children aged 5–7 used more energy if their playgrounds were painted with brightly coloured markings to encourage them to exercise at playtime.

The scientists used specialised equipment to measure the children's pulse rate in the last minute of four activities: lying quietly (8 minutes), sitting upright (8 minutes), walking at 4 km/hour (4 minutes) and running at 7 km/hour (4 minutes).

They found the average pulse rate in beats per minute (bpm) for boys and for girls each time, and recorded the results in a table.

Exercise	Boys' pulse rate/bpm	Girls' pulse rate/bpm
Lying	88	95
Sitting	99	103
Walking	115	128
Running	159	166

Questions

1. What was the lowest heart rate recorded in the table?

2. What exercise was being taken at that time?

3. Would you expect the heart rate to be low when that exercise was being taken? Explain your answer.

4. What was the difference between the boys' heart rate and the girls' heart rate when they were walking?

5. What was the maximum heart rate recorded?

6. Why do you think the heart rate was so high at that time?

7. By how much did the boys' heart rate increase from when they were walking to when they were running?

8. Draw a bar chart to show the results for boys and for girls.

9. Do you think the heart rate would have increased even more if the boys and girls had walked or run for more than 4 minutes?

10. What can you say about the overall pattern of heart rate and exercise from looking at the data?

HANDLING SCIENCE DATA YEAR 5

PULSE RATE RETURNING TO NORMAL

National Curriculum Science KS2 PoS Sc2: 2d
QCA Science Unit 5A: Keeping healthy
Scottish 5–14 Guidelines The processes of life – Level C; Physical health – Level C

HOW TO GATHER THE DATA

It is important that you spend time with the children helping them to measure their pulse rate, which is measured as the number of beats in a minute. If the pulse is taken by hand, the thumb should be used to support the wrist while two fingertips are used to feel the pulse – otherwise, the pulse in the thumb may prevent accurate counting of the pulse in the wrist. Timers that measure in seconds should be used. At first, ask the children to measure and record their pulse rate several times while they are sitting down – ask them why the rate may be different each time they measure it. Then ask them to work out the average pulse rate of the whole class, or of the girls and the boys in the class separately.

The investigation of changes in pulse rate is not easy to carry out, as many children find it difficult to record their pulse rate accurately. A chart such as the one on page 11 will be useful for reference. It is also valuable to have a classroom assistant or parent helper to support the children in finding and counting their pulse. The exercises the children undertake should be normal activities such as running around the playground or on the spot. If the school has a digital pulse meter, this could be used to measure a number of children's pulse rates at the same time.

Answers

1. approximately 70 bpm
2. approximately 140 bpm
3. Their pulse rate had increased.
4. 115 bpm
5. 3 minutes
6. The difference is very slight at all times.
7. The boys and girls would be expected to show a similar pattern, as they are the same age and have the same body mass, height and so on.
8. The pulse rate increased rapidly during exercise, then began to fall again when the exercise stopped and decreased to the normal level over a period of three minutes.
9. During exercise the muscles that are active need more glucose and oxygen from the blood, so the heart needs to pump more blood to the muscles.
10. Yes. The heart would have needed to pump the blood to the muscles even faster, so the pulse rate would have risen higher and would then take longer to return to normal.
11. The children became hotter and their breathing rate increased.

THE SCIENCE BEHIND THE DATA

For notes on the heart and the increase in pulse rate during exercise, see page 10. This activity focuses on the process of recovery following exercise. The time taken for the heart rate to return to its resting level is comparable to the time taken for it to increase during exercise. One factor that slows down recovery is that during rapid exercise, while the heart rate is still increasing, the active muscles depend on anaerobic respiration (without oxygen), which produces lactic acid and can result in cramp. Oxygen is needed to reconvert the lactic acid to glucose in the blood. During prolonged exercise, or following brief exercise, the heart has to do additional work in order to correct this 'oxygen debt'.

Pulse rate returning to normal

Eight boys and eight girls in Class 5 measured their pulse rates when they were sitting in the classroom. Then they ran around the playground for three minutes before measuring their pulse rates again. They repeated the measurements at one-minute intervals after they had stopped running.

They worked out their average pulse rate for each time in beats per minute (bpm) and recorded the results as a line graph.

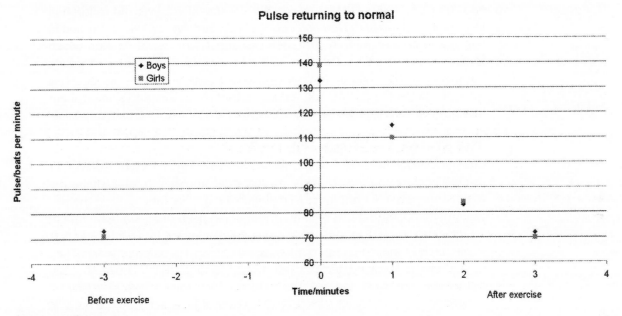

Questions

1. What was the girls' average pulse rate before exercise?

2. What was the girls' average pulse rate immediately after they had stopped exercising?

3. What had happened to their pulse rate when they exercised?

4. What was the boys' average pulse rate one minute after they had stopped exercising?

5. How long did it take for the pulse rates of all the children to return to the level they were at before exercise?

6. Was there a difference between the boys' pulse rates and the girls' pulse rates?

7. Did the pulse rates of the boys and the girls show a similar pattern? Why?

8. Can you describe this pattern?

9. Why does exercise affect the pulse rate?

10. Do you think it would take longer for the pulse rate to return to normal if the children had exercised for 5 minutes? Explain your answer.

11. What else do you think happened to the children when they exercised?

HANDLING SCIENCE DATA YEAR 5

FOODS TO STAY HEALTHY

National Curriculum Science KS2 PoS Sc2: 2b
QCA Science Unit 5A: Keeping healthy
Scottish 5–14 Guidelines Physical health – Level C

HOW TO GATHER THE DATA

These data are taken from a real survey (Hackett, AF, Gibbon, M, Stratton, G and Hamill, E, 2000, 'Dietary intake of 9–10 and 11–12 year old children in Liverpool', *Public Health Nutrition Vol. 5*, 2002). Surveys like this, published in health and exercise journals, are useful secondary sources of data on which to base an investigation. The data have been simplified, and some foods are not included. The children in your class could carry out a 24-hour or 2-day survey of all the things they eat, recording them in a diary and splitting them into positive and negative marker foods to compare with the data opposite.

THE SCIENCE BEHIND THE DATA

Children need to be familiar with the scientific meaning of the word 'diet'. Our diet is everything that we eat. A healthy (balanced and varied) diet contains the right amounts of the right foods to maintain our bodies' functions, so that we can grow properly and stay healthy. The children need to be aware that there are different groups of foods (such as fruits, vegetables and meat/fish), and that starch, fat and sugar are important substances found in different foods. They do not have to know the terms 'carbohydrate' and 'protein' – however, they will see these terms on food packages, so you may want to explain them.

Recommended daily allowances (RDAs) cannot be exact; but as a general guide, a child in Key Stage 2 should consume 8000kJ of energy and 30g of protein per day in the approximate proportions: 8 of starch, 4 of vegetables, 3 of fruits, 3 of dairy products, 3 of meat/fish/beans, and small amounts of fat and sugar.

Ask the children to plan how they could alter their diet to make it more healthy. Discuss how important it is to eat some foods from different groups each day. Stress the value of eating more of the positive marker foods and less of the negative marker foods (though some negative marker foods, such as baked beans, have nutritional value). The topic could be planned to coincide with a 'healthy eating week' at school, with the school tuck shop selling fruit rather than other snacks. The discussion could range from 'Are you eating a balanced diet?' to comparisons with RDAs. Links could be made to tooth decay, which is related to the amount of sugar in the diet. Be sensitive to the social issues encompassed by this topic: children's opportunities to choose what they eat may be limited.

Answers

1. Fruit
2. Low-fat sausages or burgers.
3. 30%
4. Children may suggest brown bread, pasta, rice, oat cereals, grilled fish and so on.
5. a) Yes b) No
6. Fizzy drinks
7. Diet fruit drinks
8. 37%
9. Puddings
10. Children may suggest most fast foods, crisps, ice cream and so on – anything with an excess of fat or sugar.
11. a) 37% b) 17%
12. a) Fruit, vegetables, high-fibre cereals, diet fruit drinks and so on. b) Chips, fatty foods, chocolate, fizzy drinks and so on. Discuss this with the children so they can justify their choices.

Foods to stay healthy

A team of researchers carried out a survey of what 4000 children aged 9–10, living in a large city, ate in one particular day (over 24 hours). They separated the foods into **positive marker foods** (foods that we should eat more of because they are important for health and growth) and **negative marker foods** (foods we should eat less of, because they contain a lot of fats and sugars).

They recorded their results in two bar charts.

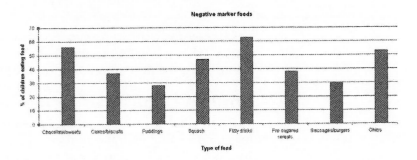

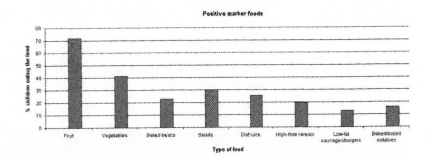

Questions

1. Which positive marker food was eaten by the most children?

2. Which positive marker food was eaten by the least children?

3. What percentage of the children ate salads in the 24 hours?

4. Are there any other foods we should eat more of (foods that are good for our health) that are not recorded in the chart?

5. Look at the bar chart for negative marker foods. Are they mostly: **a)** fats and sugars? **b)** foods for growth?

6. Which negative marker food did the most children eat or drink?

7. Use the list of positive marker foods to suggest a healthier alternative to this negative marker food.

8. What percentage of children ate cakes and biscuits?

9. What food did 28% of the children eat?

10. Are there any other foods we should eat less of that are not recorded in the chart?

11. Compare the two charts. What percentage more of children ate **a)** chips rather than baked or boiled potatoes? **b)** sausages and burgers rather than the low-fat alternative?

12. From looking at the survey, **a)** what foods do you think you should eat more of? **b)** what foods do you think you should eat less of?

HANDLING SCIENCE DATA YEAR 5

IS SMOKING BAD FOR HEALTH?

National Curriculum Science KS2 PoS Sc2: 2g
QCA Science Unit 5A: Keeping healthy
Scottish 5–14 Guidelines Physical health – Level D

HOW TO GATHER THE DATA

There are a number of websites listing national statistics and research findings regarding the long-term effects of smoking on health. The data shown opposite have been simplified from a research paper: Richard G Rogers and E Powell-Griner (1991) 'Life expectancies of cigarette smokers and non-smokers in the United States', *Soc. Sci. Med. 32* pp.1151–1159. Other useful sites include the *British Medical Journal* (www.bmj.com), and the new (1999) British government statistics site (www.statistics.gov.uk) – on the public health section of this site, you can find other data on the effects of smoking such as 'Which age group of the population smoke the most?' and 'Cigarette smoking among secondary school pupils'.

THE SCIENCE BEHIND THE DATA

The effect of smoking on health is an issue that needs to be tackled sensitively in the classroom, because some of the children may have lost relatives due to smoking-related diseases such as lung cancer or respiratory problems. However, recent reports have indicated that teenage smoking is on the increase, so it is important for children to become aware of the relevant health issues while in primary school. You could ask someone from the local health promotion unit to come in and talk to the children about this and other health-related issues.

Tobacco smoke contains a high proportion of toxic chemicals. The tar in tobacco smoke damages the cilia (tiny hairs) in the windpipe. The cilia normally remove bacteria and dirt; if they stop working, bacteria, mucus and dirt can build up deep inside the lungs and cause chest infections such as bronchitis. Eventually, the alveoli (tiny air sacs inside the lungs) become blocked and damaged, the surface area of the lungs is reduced, and it becomes harder to breathe. Tobacco smoke also contains carbon monoxide, which can bind to haemoglobin in the blood as oxygen does, preventing some oxygen transport – the blood of smokers is less efficient in carrying oxygen than the blood of non-smokers. Other chemicals in tobacco smoke can cause lung cancer.

The difference made to life expectancy by smoking becomes less as age increases. This is partly because other health problems become prevalent in later life (so smoking makes less difference), and partly because the damage caused by smoking is cumulative (the earlier you start, the more harm it will do).

Answers

1. 42 years
2. 47 years
3. 5 years
4. 45
5. 65
6. 10 years
7. 12 years
8. 2 years
9. People who live to 75 will only generally be expected to live another 10 or so years, since they are likely to suffer from a range of medical problems that affect life expectancy. You will need to discuss this with the children.
10. The non-smokers.
11. Encourage the children to respond with more than 'smoking is bad for you'. You will need to discuss the reasons why smoking is bad for health. It contains tar and other chemicals that affect the lungs, making it more difficult to breathe. It can also damage other parts of the body, including the heart and the blood.
12. Young women can have babies, and if they smoke it will affect the baby's health. Again, you may need to discuss this with the children – they may have seen warnings about smoking and pregnancy on advertisement boards or cigarette packets.

Is smoking bad for health?

A group of children found some data on the Internet that compared the life expectancies of American women who smoke and American women who do not smoke. Life expectancy was given as how many **more** years the people in each age group were expected to live.

The children entered the data in a spreadsheet and plotted a graph.

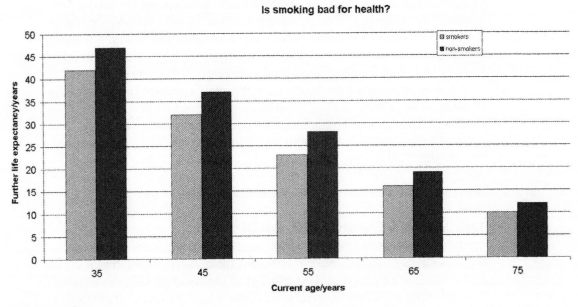

Questions

1. How many more years are women of 35 who smoke expected to live?

2. How many more years are women of 35 who do not smoke expected to live?

3. How much longer are 35-year-old non-smokers expected to live than 35-year-old smokers?

4. How old are smokers with a further life expectancy of 32 years?

5. How old are non-smokers with a further life expectancy of 18 years?

6. How many more years are 75-year-old smokers expected to live?

7. How many more years are 75-year-old non-smokers expected to live?

8. How much longer are 75-year-old non-smokers expected to live than 75-year-old smokers?

9. Why do you think this difference is less than for 35-year-old women?

10. Generally, which group is expected to live longer: the smokers or the non-smokers?

11. Can you explain why?

12. Smoking is particularly dangerous for young women. Can you explain why?

GERMINATING SEEDS

National Curriculum Science KS2 PoS Sc2: 3a, d
QCA Science Unit 5B: Life cycles.
Scottish 5–14 Guidelines The processes of life – Level B

HOW TO GATHER THE DATA

You will need to collect some plastic trays and plastic bags (or long plastic sandwich containers), and give each group about 50 fast-growing seeds such as barley or grass seeds. Some groups can place their seeds on a dry paper towel inside a plastic container. If you are using plastic bags, blow them up so there is a lot of air inside (make sure the children do this safely). Brainstorm where to put the seeds with the children. Encourage them to suggest a range of warm/cold, light/dark places and to give reasons for their choices. Give them an opportunity to observe their seeds once a day for about 5 days, and to record their observations about the colour and length of the roots and shoots. After 5 days, they can examine the seeds more closely and count the number with shoots (observing their appearance and length), the number with roots, and the number that have not germinated at all.

THE SCIENCE BEHIND THE DATA

Seeds need water and warmth to germinate. Dry seeds will not germinate under any conditions of light or warmth. You will need to emphasise that if water and warmth are both present, seeds kept in the dark will germinate. Many children, especially if they have not investigated the conditions for germination, will suggest that seeds need light to germinate. In fact, some seeds germinate better in dark conditions. Having done the investigation, the children can relate their findings to some real-life situations: many seeds germinate underground, in the dark.

The seed coat, or testa, is waterproof, but water enters the seed through a tiny hole, the micropile. The seed coat splits and the root and shoot start to grow. In a barley seed, the shoot and the root both emerge underground from the seed coat. This is known as hypogeal germination. (Some seeds, such as sunflower seeds, have a shoot that starts to grow above ground. This is known as epigeal germination.)

Answers

1. The warm windowsill.
2. 37
3. The seeds may have not been left long enough for all of them to germinate. Discuss with the children whether all the seeds would eventually germinate. (Not all seeds do.)
4. On the warm windowsill and the colder windowsill.
5. The seeds grown in the warmer place had longer shoots and roots.
6. The seeds in the fridge and the dry seeds. The dry seeds did not germinate because there was no water. The seeds in the fridge were too cold to germinate.
7. 16
8. These shoots were yellow because there was no light, and long because they were growing to try to reach the light.
9. Warmth and water.
10. Yes. The differences between the results for different batches are clear.
11. The number of seeds, the number of days the seeds were left to germinate, the size of the container, the wetness of the towel.
12. Discuss the likely germination conditions of different seeds. Draw on the children's experiences – for example, they may have noticed how easily sycamore seeds grow in lawns. Discuss seed germination in other climates: many Alpine plants need to be exposed to very cold conditions before they can germinate (this ensures that the seeds germinate at times of the year when they can survive and grow). In many dry places (such as semi-desert), very little grows until it rains – and then seeds that have been dormant for years start to grow suddenly.

Germinating seeds

Scott, Angus, Rosie and Catrina helped their teacher, Miss McIntosh, to investigate the question: *Which is the best place to keep seeds in order for them to germinate?* Each child counted out 50 barley seeds and placed them on a wet paper towel inside a plastic container. They sealed their containers and put them in different places. Miss McIntosh placed her 50 seeds on a dry paper towel inside a plastic container.

This graph shows their results.

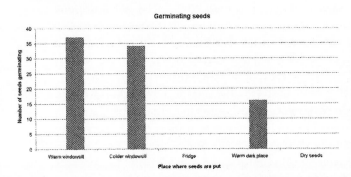

The children recorded the temperature of each place, and observed the appearance of the shoots and roots.

Warm windowsill (22°C) – green shoots 5cm long, long white roots.
Colder windowsill (12°C) – green shoots 1cm long, clump of short white roots.
Warm cupboard (26°C) – yellow shoots 10cm long, long white roots.
Fridge (4°C) – no shoots, no roots.
Dry seeds – no shoots, no roots.

Questions

1. In which place did the most seeds germinate?

2. How many seeds germinated there?

3. Why didn't all 50 seeds germinate in this place?

4. In which two places did a similar number of seeds germinate?

5. What was the main difference observed between the young plants grown in these two places? (Look at the children's notebook.)

6. Which batches of seeds did not germinate? Can you explain why?

7. How many seeds germinated in the warm, dark place (a cupboard)?

8. Why were the shoots produced from these seeds long and yellow?

9. From the data and your answers so far, what things do you think are needed for seeds to germinate?

10. Do you think 50 seeds were enough for the children to be able to compare one place with another? Explain your answer.

11. What things should the children have kept the same to make their investigation fair?

12. Barley seeds were used in this investigation. Do you think that other seeds would behave in the same way?

POLLINATION

National Curriculum Science KS2 PoS Sc2: 3d
QCA Science Unit 5B: Life cycles
Scottish 5–14 Guidelines Processes of life – Level D

HOW TO GATHER THE DATA

The Programme of Study for Sc1 (Scientific enquiry) in the English National Curriculum encourages the use of secondary sources of data. The data shown opposite are taken from a genuine scientific experiment ('Nectar and petal attraction for pollinators on artificial flowers', Anna-Karin Ivarsson and Jessica Larsson, 2000)* that was carried out in the Rio Clarillo National Reserve in Chile under constant sunny conditions, in a Mediterranean-type climate. Which sounds like good justification for a scientific research project!

I have been to schools that have tried this investigation, but I do not know what the outcome was. Many different factors can affect the results, and the children will have to be meticulous about collecting their data. Californian poppies are very attractive to hoverflies, Michaelmas daisies to butterflies and clover to bees. The investigation works better when there are plenty of insects about and the weather is dry and sunny. The 'nectar' used in this investigation was honey, and the different-coloured petals were made from painted (non-toxic) paper. (The children could use coloured crêpe paper.)

Answers

1. Red

2. Blue

3. The blue flower was visited by the most bees, so being this colour would give a flower the best chance of being pollinated. (Encourage full explanations.)

4. Bees visit flowers to find nectar, which they need as food. Nectar is a sugar solution, so it is a high-energy food and is easily digested.

5. To find the nectar, a bee crawls down to the nectary at the base of the flower. As the bee goes past the stamen, pollen sticks to it. When the bee visits another flower of the same species, the pollen sticks to the stigma and begins to pollinate it. This leads to fertilisation of the second plant.

6. Answers might include: using the same size petals, the same material, the same amount of time for observation, the same weather conditions, the same time of day.

7. Petals

8. Very few bees visited the two flowers without petals (with and without nectar), but many visited the two flowers with petals (with and without nectar).

9. For comparison, by showing what would happen if neither factor were present. The correct term is 'as a control', but the children may not be familiar with this.

10. The two most common additional features are markings that lead to the centre of the flower and scent.

THE SCIENCE BEHIND THE DATA

Insects need to be as efficient as possible in their search for nectar for food, so they are selective about what flowers they visit. Colour and scent have been shown to be the two most important factors. Different colours tend to attract different insects:

■ beetles are attracted to white, brown and other dull colours

■ flies are attracted to dull colours

■ bees are attracted to blue, white or yellow flowers, often with distinct markings

■ moths are attracted to white or pale-coloured flowers

■ butterflies are attracted to red flowers.

If their preferred colour is not readily available, insects will go to other colours. Some insects, such as bees, can also 'see' ultraviolet (UV) light, and it is thought that the blue flowers used in the study might have reflected a high amount of UV radiation. This may explain the relative popularity of blue and white flowers in the study.

* For details, see www.entom.slu.se/ent13

Pollination

Two scientists were investigating how flowers attract insects. They wanted to find out which was more important to the insects: petals or nectar. They also wanted to find out whether the colour of the petals made a difference. They set up two different investigations.

Investigation 1

The scientists set up paper flowers in four different colours in a nature park on a sunny day. They watched to see how many times bees visited each of the four flowers.

This graph shows their results.

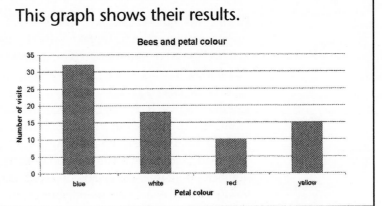

Questions

1. Which was the least popular colour?

2. Which is the best colour for a flower to be?

3. Explain your answer to Question 2.

4. Why do bees visit flowers?

5. Describe how bees pollinate flowers.

6. What three things should the scientists have done to make this a fair test?

Investigation 2

Then the scientists set up paper flowers with and without petals and with and without added nectar. They watched how many times bees visited each of the four flowers.

This graph shows their results.

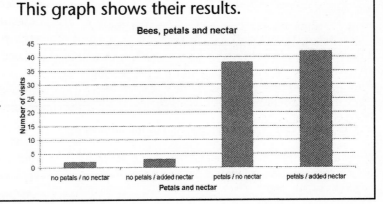

7. Which is more important for attracting bees: petals or nectar?

8. Explain how you decided this.

9. Why did the scientists use one flower with no petals and no nectar?

10. Examine a flower (or a picture of one). Can you see anything else that might persuade insects to visit them?

HANDLING SCIENCE DATA YEAR 5

SYCAMORE SEEDS

> **National Curriculum Science** KS2 PoS Sc2: 3d
> **QCA Science** Unit 5B: Life cycles
> **Scottish 5–14 Guidelines** Processes of Life – Level D

HOW TO GATHER THE DATA

Simple templates can be made for the children to make and investigate model 'winged seeds' of different sizes or shapes, or made from different materials. All of these factors will affect the time it takes the seed to fall. When the models fall, they do not always spin well, so the children will need to decide whether each result is reliable or not. In addition, there is a small difference in results due to fluctuating air currents, so taking an average of several results is appropriate. However, the models give quite consistent results. The children will need a stopwatch measuring to the nearest 0.01s in order to record significant differences. Any children not confident with decimals can simply use the numbers and still identify a meaningful pattern.

THE SCIENCE BEHIND THE DATA

Seeds need to be dispersed because for a new seed to grow healthily, it will need a good source of water, nutrients and light. If the new seed is near the parent plant, it has to compete with an established plant (and other seeds) for water and nutrients from the soil. Also, the leaves of the parent plant may reduce the amount of light getting through to the newly germinated seed and hinder its growth.

Seeds can be dispersed in several ways. Sycamore and dandelion seeds rely on wind dispersal. Animals can disperse seeds by eating them, where the seed is contained in an edible fruit or nut. The hard-coated seed passes through the digestive system unharmed. Seeds or fruits such as burdock and goosegrass are hooked; they stick to animal fur and are carried away. In the pea family, the seeds grow in pods that explode and send the seeds some distance from the parent plant. Sweet peas will grow quickly in the summer term, and can be used to demonstrate this type of seed dispersal.

Wind-dispersed seeds will travel further if they can stay in the air for longer. Spinning keeps the seed in the air, so it has more chance of being blown away from the parent plant. The graph shown opposite indicates that there is an optimum size for 'spinning'. Smaller seeds do not encounter enough air resistance, whereas larger seeds are too heavy.

Answers

1. 3.3s
2. 50mm
3. 2.0s
4. The 200mm and 250mm seeds both took 2.0s, so it is likely that larger seeds will do the same.
5. The point should be at 2.2s on the graph. The child should draw a continuation of the curve, not a straight line, for the added segment.
6. 75mm, because this wingspan takes the longest time to fall. More knowledgeable children may be able to explain that this benefits the seed because it can be blown away and reach a new place where there is less competition for water and nutrients. They may also suggest that if the seed falls slowly, it will not get damaged. Any reflective answer should be given credit.
7. ABy adding up all the times and dividing by the number of seeds (5).
8. To obtain data that are more reliable than for a single seed. Note that **reliable** means you are sure about your data, whereas **accurate** means how well the stopwatch keeps time and **precise** means measuring to 0.01s rather than 0.1s. So using an average will not make the data any more accurate or precise. Whether you discuss these distinctions will depend on the capability of the child.
9. The same material for model seeds, dropped from the same height. (Not the same stopwatch, because they all use the same units.)
10. Look for appropriate sections of the planning sheets (photocopiable pages 60–3) completed according to the child's chosen investigation.

Sycamore seeds

Chloe noticed that when sycamore seeds fell off a tree, they started to spin round. Her friend Tom asked: "If they have bigger wings, will they spin for longer before they hit the ground?"

"I don't think so," said Chloe. Miss Falola thought this was something the class could investigate. Each group made a different-sized sycamore seed out of paper and timed how long it took to fall. They tested each model seed five times and took an average.

This is a graph of the class's results.

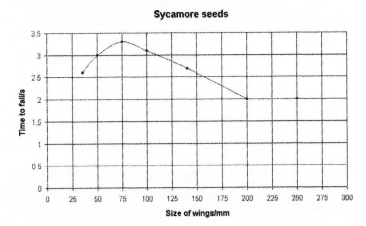

Questions

1. How long did the seed with a wingspan of 75mm take to fall?

2. How big was the seed that took 3.0s to fall?

3. How long do you think a 300mm seed will take to fall?

4. Explain how you worked out your answer.

5. Draw a point on the graph to predict the time it would take a 25mm seed to fall. Connect it up to the rest of the curve.

6. Which is the 'best' size for a model sycamore seed? Explain your choice.

7. Explain how the children worked out the average time for each seed.

8. Why do you think they tested each seed five times and took an average?

9. Give two things the children should have kept the same to make their investigation fair.

10. Think of another investigation that you could do with model sycamore seeds. Write a plan for it. Your plan should include:

- what you will change each time
- what you will measure each time
- what you will keep the same each time
- a blank table for your results, showing the headings and units
- a blank graph for your results – label the axes correctly and give the units.

HANDLING SCIENCE DATA YEAR 5

A GROWING BABY

> *National Curriculum Science* KS2 PoS Sc2: 2f
> *QCA Science* Unit 5B: Life cycles
> *Scottish 5–14 Guidelines* The processes of life – Levels B, D

HOW TO GATHER THE DATA

The data shown opposite are based on clinical records. It is highly unlikely that you will have access to a newborn baby and appropriate equipment in order to generate similar data. The children may have seen babies being weighed in a clinic, where a special baby balance is used: it has a very large pan, so the baby cannot fall out. A local health centre or midwife could give you information about the weights of babies at and following birth. Perhaps one of the children in your class may have a newborn brother or sister, whose mother could bring the baby into school. The children could search the Internet, using the key words 'baby birth weight', to find a number of useful sites.

THE SCIENCE BEHIND THE DATA

When the baby is in the womb, it derives all its nutrition directly through the umbilical cord. At this stage, the baby's digestive system is not operating fully. The baby will build up layers of fat in the few weeks prior to a full-term birth. When the baby is born and is being breast-fed, the mother's milk does not flow properly until about two or three days after feeding starts. Also, the baby's digestive system needs time to start functioning fully, so the baby uses the supply of fat that it has built up as a source of food until its digestive system is fully operational and it is receiving a full supply of milk. While the baby is using up this fat, its mass decreases. As the baby's feeding develops, its body mass starts to increase again.

Answers

1. 3kg

2. 2.5kg (+/– 0.1kg)

3. 3 weeks

4. The baby's mass decreases after birth (for about 10 days), then increases again. After about 3 weeks, her mass increases steadily. This question is designed to encourage the children to extract as much information as possible from the graph. Encourage them to interpret and summarise the data, looking for trends, rather than simply to describe individual points on the graph (for example, 'The baby had a mass of 3kg at birth').

5. 2kg

6. Just under 1kg

7. Approximately 7.6kg. The child should find the point by extending the curve.

8. Approximately 4kg heavier

9. Accept any sensible suggestions, such as: the baby is not feeding properly at the start, but once it is feeding properly it increases in mass. The children do not need to know this explanation – but the question encourages them to use the information they have, together with their own knowledge, to draw reasonable conclusions.

A growing baby

Soon after babies are born, their 'weight'
– strictly speaking, their mass – changes.
Mass is measured in kilograms (kg).

This graph shows how the mass of one
baby changed over a period of 6 weeks
after she was born.

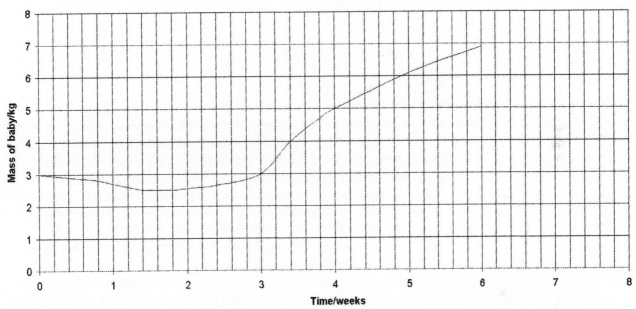

A growing baby

Mass of baby/kg (y-axis: 0–8)

Time/weeks (x-axis: 0–8)

Questions

1. What was the mass of the baby at birth?

2. What was the lowest mass the baby reached?

3. How long was there between birth and the point when the baby regained
her birth mass?

4. Describe in detail what the graph tells you about the mass of the baby
over the first 6 weeks.

5. How much mass did the baby gain between 3 and 4 weeks?

6. How much mass did she gain between 5 and 6 weeks?

7. Draw in a point to predict the baby's mass at 7 weeks.

8. How much heavier is the baby at 6 weeks than when
she was newly born?

9. Can you suggest any reasons why a baby's mass goes down at first and
then increases?

HANDLING SCIENCE DATA YEAR 5

SOAKING WET

National Curriculum Science KS2 PoS Sc3: 1e
QCA Science Unit 5C: Gases around us
Scottish 5–14 Guidelines Science Materials from Earth: Level C

HOW TO GATHER THE DATA

This is a simple activity that children can use to practise investigative skills. It gives straightforward results that can usually be related to the materials being tested. You will need to take precautions for the use of dripping wet materials in the classroom. We have used a constant mass of material (5g) rather than a constant size, since sponges are usually thicker than cloths. The children may experience some difficulty in deciding when the material has stopped dripping, but they can weigh all the samples at the same level of 'drippiness' – they can decide what is consistent.

THE SCIENCE BEHIND THE DATA

Materials that have holes in, allowing water to soak through them, are called 'porous'. In talking about rocks, the word 'permeable' is often used. This activity can be used as a preparation for work on rocks and soils, since it demonstrates air bubbles leaving a porous material in a fairly obvious way. Gases can easily be made to flow. When the sponge is squeezed, air flows out and the material can be compressed into a very small volume – therefore, most of the space taken up by the material is occupied by air. When the sponge is squeezed, the air comes out (the bubbles are evidence of this). If the material is released underwater, the water flows into the holes because a liquid can easily change its shape.

The three states of matter can be explained in terms of their particles. In a solid the particles are in fixed positions relative to each other, but the structure can usually bend and twist. In a liquid the particles are not fixed and can flow past each other. In a gas the particles are free to move around, so they are easily expelled from the spaces in a porous solid material.

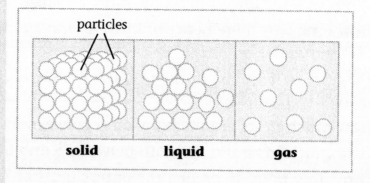

Answers

1. To make the test fair, since using more material would mean that more water was absorbed.
2. Accept any sensible suggestions, such as: squeezing out all of the air; deciding when the material has stopped dripping enough to be weighed.
3. Natural sponge
4. Face cloth
5. Kitchen sponge
6. Natural sponge
7. The water soaks into the air spaces. The natural sponge took up the most water, so it must have had the most spaces with air in.
8. The children may suggest things used to absorb water at home or in the classroom, such as a plastic bath sponge or a paper towel.
9.

Type of material	Amount of water/g
kitchen cloth	90
kitchen sponge	110
natural sponge	140
face cloth	70
towel	80

Soaking wet

Jordan and Sadika were investigating gases. They were looking at different spongy materials to see whether they had gases in them. "They've got holes in, but I can't see any gas," said Sadika. "Well, won't there be air in the holes? That's a gas," said Jordan. "And when you squeeze them underwater, bubbles come out."

Their teacher asked them to find out which material held the most gas. They took 5g of each material, squeezed it underwater, then let it soak up water. They took the material out of the water, let it stop dripping, then weighed the wet material.

This graph shows their results.

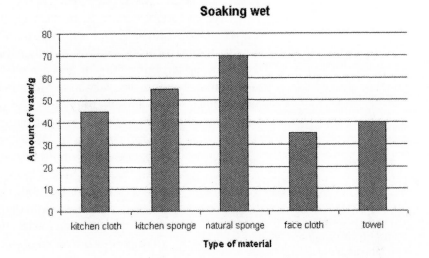

Questions

1. Why did they always test 5g of each material?

2. What difficulties might Jordan and Sadika have experienced in doing this investigation well?

3. Which material soaked up the most water?

4. Which material soaked up the least water?

5. Which material soaked up 55g of water?

6. Which material do you think had the most holes in?

7. Explain your answer to Question 6.

8. Name two other materials that the children could have tested.

9. Draw a table to show what results the children would have got if they had used 10g of material each time.

HANDLING SCIENCE DATA YEAR 5

HELIUM BALLOONS

National Curriculum Science KS2 PoS Sc3: 1e; Sc4: 2b, e
QCA Science Unit 5C: Gases around us
Scottish 5–14 Guidelines Materials from Earth – Level C; Forces and their effects – Level E

HOW TO GATHER THE DATA

If you are going to do this experiment in practice, you need to have a friendly supplier of small amounts of helium. Information about helium is available on the Internet at www.howstuffworks.com/helium.htm (this is a US site, so you will need to convert the units to make use of their data). Coincidentally (and usefully), 1 litre of helium can lift approximately 1g in air. A standard size of helium balloon can be used and inflated to different sizes.

THE SCIENCE BEHIND THE DATA

When we talk about helium being 'lighter' than air, what we mean is that a given volume of helium has less mass than the same volume of air. This is because helium particles have less mass than the nitrogen and oxygen particles that make up air, but a litre (or any given volume) of any gas contains the same number of particles. A balloon full of helium is therefore lighter than a balloon full of air. As a result, the upthrust of the air on the balloon is greater than its weight pulling it down, so the balloon rises.

Upthrust is a result of the effect of gravity. Just as the pressure on the bottom brick in a pile of bricks is greater than that on the top brick, the pressure within a fluid (a liquid or a gas) is greater the further down you go, because of the cumulative weight of the particles above. The pressure difference between the top (lower pressure) and the bottom (higher pressure) of an object results in an upward force that tends to make the object rise through the fluid, unless its own weight can balance the upthrust.

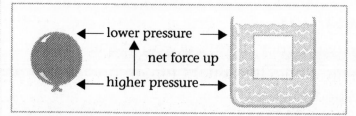

A helium balloon rising through air will encounter air resistance, resulting in a steady rise (as with an object falling under the influence of gravity) rather than an acceleration – but it will continue to rise until it hits the ceiling. Attaching a mass to the balloon can balance the upthrust and so hold the balloon in mid-air.

The greater the circumference of the helium balloon, the more helium it contains and so the more additional weight is needed to balance the upthrust. The graph is curved because the upthrust is proportional to the volume of helium, and the relationship between the volume and the circumference of a sphere is a curve.

Answers

1. 2.1g
2. 56cm
3. The larger the balloon, the more mass it can lift. (See page 6 in the Introduction for notes on comparative statements.)
4. a) 0.5g **b)** 12.3g
5.

Circumference of balloon/cm	Amount of lift/g
40	1.1
50	2.1
60	3.7
70	5.8
80	8.7

6. No: the mass lifted will be zero for very small circumferences also.
7. Almost-empty balloons will still have mass, but there will not be enough helium to lift them.
8. Helium is lighter (less dense) than air, so there is an upthrust on the balloon.
9. Some of the helium has escaped, so there is less upthrust on the balloon. The child may suggest that the helium has leaked out through the tied neck of the balloon, but in fact most of the helium will escape through the balloon material (even though helium balloons are less porous than ordinary ones).

Helium balloons

After her birthday party, Kirsty brought a helium-filled balloon into school. It floated to the ceiling in the classroom. "Can we try weighing it down with some Plasticine?" Kirsty asked. She attached some Plasticine to the balloon until it just hovered in the air.

Later, the children tried filling balloons with different amounts of helium to see how much mass each balloon could support. This line graph shows their results.

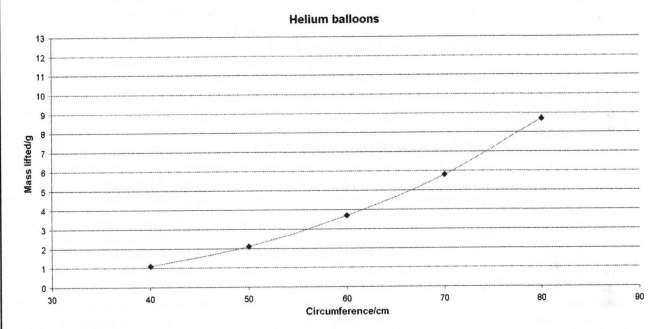

Questions

1. How much mass did a 50cm balloon lift?

2. What size of balloon would lift a 3g mass?

3. How does the size of the balloon affect the mass it can lift?

4. Continue the line to predict the mass that would be lifted by **a)** a 30cm balloon? **b)** a 90cm balloon?

5. Design and fill in a table of the children's results.

6. The graph does not show results for smaller balloons. Would you expect the mass lifted to be zero only when the balloon's circumference is zero?

7. Give a scientific reason for your answer to Question 6.

8. Why does a helium-filled balloon float upwards?

9. After two days, the helium-filled balloons had become smaller and did not float on the ceiling any more. Can you explain why this happened?

HANDLING SCIENCE DATA YEAR 5

FIZZY DRINKS CAN

> **National Curriculum Science** KS2 PoS Sc3: 1e, 3e
> **QCA Science** Unit 5C: Gases around us
> **Scottish 5–14 Guidelines** Materials from Earth – Level C

HOW TO GATHER THE DATA

It is very difficult to demonstrate to children that a gas has mass, but this investigation is one of the best ways to do it. You will need an accurate balance to carry out this investigation. Balances that weigh to the nearest 0.1g can be obtained for use in primary schools for about £50–80 (it's worth shopping around), and are a good investment. Alternatively, a balance could be borrowed from a nearby secondary school. Note that because the mass of the solution changes only very slowly, the readings will appear to change in 'steps' as each loss of 0.01g shows up on the scales. The graph has been adjusted to remove this effect.

Groups of children could do the experiment in turn, each investigating a different type of fizzy drink. The drinks will lose most of their gas in about one hour. You could open another can to let the children taste the drink from it on opening (when it is fizzy) and after an hour (when it is 'flat').

THE SCIENCE BEHIND THE DATA

Before doing this investigation, you and the children should discuss the contents of the can and what happens when it is opened. Most children will know that the drink is fizzy because of the gas trapped in it, and that most of the gas is released immediately after the can is opened. Carbon dioxide is forced into the water-based drink under pressure, because it is more soluble at higher pressures. When the can or bottle is opened, the pressure is released and a lot of the carbon dioxide is immediately forced out of the solution.

The 'fizz' is the bubbles of gas that appear in the liquid. This happens because each tiny bubble that forms provides a surface at which dissolved carbon dioxide can escape from the solution, so the bubble grows until it is visible. As the bubbles rise, the pressure drops, which also causes them to expand. Bubble formation within a 'fizzy' solution can be observed with lemonade in a small, clear, colourless plastic bottle.

After the initial escape of gas, the dissolved gas escapes steadily into the atmosphere (because the level of carbon dioxide in the atmosphere is quite low, so carbon dioxide particles leave the water more frequently than they enter it). Within an hour, almost all of the dissolved carbon dioxide has left the water and escaped from the container.

Answers

1. The gas trapped inside a fizzy drink can does not have much mass, so the differences to be measured are very small. An accurate balance is needed to make these measurements.

2. 1g

3. 20 minutes

4. The gas that was dissolved in the water, making the drink fizzy, gradually escaped into the air.

5. In the first minute after the can was opened.

6. The gas was kept under pressure inside the can, forcing more of it to dissolve in the water than would normally be possible. As soon as the can was opened, a large amount of gas escaped from the water and into the atmosphere.

7. The can's mass would stay about the same mass, as most of the gas had already escaped.

8. The drink would taste 'flat' (no longer fizzy), as most of the gas had escaped.

9. Carbon dioxide (often the ingredient 'carbonated water' is marked on the can).

Fizzy drinks can

Jenny wanted to find out what happens to the gas inside a fizzy drink can when it is opened. She placed a can on an electronic balance that weighed to the nearest 0.1g. She opened the ringpull slowly, then recorded the mass of the can every 5 minutes.

Jenny recorded her results in a graph.

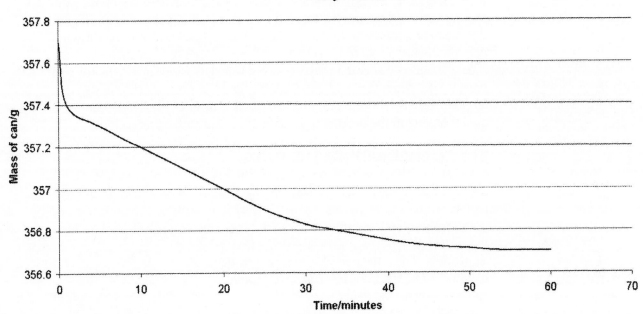

Questions

1. Why did Jenny have to use a balance weighing to the nearest 0.1g?

2. How much mass was lost from the can (or its contents) in 1 hour?

3. How long did it take for the mass of the can to reach 357g?

4. Why did the can (or its contents) lose mass?

5. At what time did the can lose the most mass?

6. Why do you think this happened?

7. What would happen to the can's mass if Jenny left it for another hour? Can you explain why?

8. What do you think the fizzy drink would taste like at the end of an hour?

9. Try to find out what gas is put into fizzy drinks.

HANDLING SCIENCE DATA YEAR 5

EVAPORATING LIQUIDS

National Curriculum Science KS2 PoS Sc3: 2a, b, d
QCA Science Unit 5D: Changing state
Scottish 5–14 Guidelines Changing materials – Levels B, C

HOW TO GATHER THE DATA

The liquids used in this investigation are readily available, but a friendly secondary school would be able to supply you with ethanol (for aftershave) and propanone (for nail varnish remover). Lighter fuel could also be used if you consider it appropriate. **Safety note:** these are flammable liquids, but can be used safely by the children under supervision. They must not be placed near a naked flame. Draw the children's attention to the 'flammable' symbol on the bottles.

As ethanol and propanone are volatile liquids that flow very easily, the children will need to have the technique of using a dropper with these liquids demonstrated. It may be preferable for you to go quickly round the class and drip the volatile liquids for the children. Water is easier to manipulate, and the activity is good for encouraging fine motor skills. Five drops gives a reasonable drying time. When the children watch the liquids dry, there is no sudden cut-off point between 'moist' and 'dry'. The skill of deciding when the sample is dry by observing the process is something the children can develop.

THE SCIENCE BEHIND THE DATA

Materials are held together by forces of attraction between particles. Solids are held together by strong forces: the particles are held in a close, regular pattern. Liquids have weaker forces between the particles, which can move from one position to another. If the particles are moving rapidly and are near the surface of a liquid, they can escape from it (evaporation). The particles are now in a gaseous form: they are moving very rapidly and are far apart.

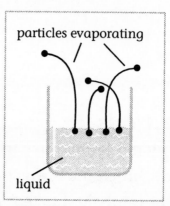

particles evaporating

liquid

Particles vibrate more, move faster and move further apart if energy (for example, heat) is supplied to them. As a liquid evaporates, the particles with the most energy escape from it – so the temperature of the liquid drops. If water (for example, rain) evaporates from your skin, the loss of energy makes your skin feel cold. A liquid will evaporate faster if the air around it is warmer, because more energy is available to make the particles move. However, any liquid can evaporate in time, whatever its temperature.

Liquids that evaporate easily are called 'volatile'. The forces between the particles are weaker in more volatile liquids. So the most volatile liquid in the investigation is nail varnish remover (propanone) and the least volatile is water.

Answers

1. Allow sensible suggestions such as: the same dropper and speed of dropping, the same paper towel (but not the same stopwatch, since time is the same for all watches).
2. Nail varnish remover.
3. This was the shortest time shown by the bars on the graph. (Discourage answers such as 'It was the smallest bar': the children should interpret the graph, not just describe it.)
4. Water
5. This was the longest time shown by the bars on the graph.
6. 10 minutes.
7. Aftershave
8. The evaporating times will be shorter.

Evaporating liquids

Some children carried out an investigation into how long different liquids take to dry up. They used a dropper to drip five drops of liquid onto a paper towel, then started a timer. They stopped the timer as soon as the spot dried up. Four different liquids were tested.

This is a graph of the children's results.

Evaporating different liquids

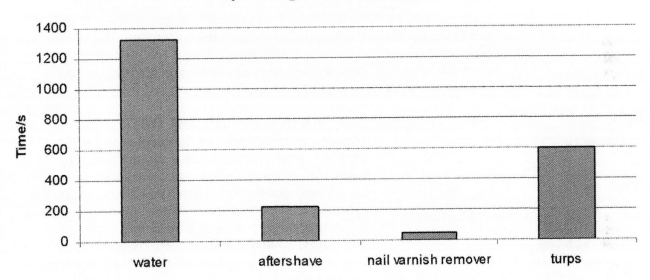

Questions

1. Make a list of the things the children should have kept the same in their investigation.

2. Which liquid was the quickest to dry up?

3. Use the graph to explain your answer to Question 2.

4. Which liquid was the slowest to dry up?

5. Use the graph to explain your answer to Question 3.

6. What is the drying time for turpentine (turps) in minutes?

7. Which of the liquid drying times is shown on the timer in the picture above?

8. What do you think will happen to the drying times if the heating is turned up and the room is warmer?

HANDLING SCIENCE DATA YEAR 5

DOES SURFACE AREA AFFECT EVAPORATION?

National Curriculum KS2 Science PoS Sc3: 2b, d
QCA Science Unit 5D: Changing state
Scottish 5–14 Guidelines Changing materials – Levels C, D

HOW TO GATHER THE DATA

You could carry out this investigation as part of a series of practical activities designed to probe and develop the children's ideas about evaporation and help them relate their scientific understanding to their everyday experience.

You will need four containers that have different cross-sectional areas. (Square or rectangular ones make calculation of the areas much easier, and link to the development of maths skills; alternatively, the children can draw around a container on $1cm^2$ paper and count the squares.) Put $100cm^3$ of water in each container. Place the containers of water in an area of the classroom (such as a windowsill) where the children can observe the changes. At the end of the week, the children should measure the amount of water left in each container accurately, using a measuring cylinder. This may introduce some small errors, as there will be a drop of water lost in the transfer – but this should not affect the pattern of results.

Answers

1. Yes
2. If there is no surface area, no evaporation will occur.
3. $10cm^3$
4. (It is a higher-order skill if the child draws a straight line of 'best fit', not a jagged line joining all the points.)
5. $42cm^3$ (approximately)
6. There have been slight errors in gathering the data. These may have been due to differences between the temperature or amount of air movement for the different containers, or they may have been due to errors in measurement (see the answer to Question 7 for more details).
7. Measuring the amount of water that had evaporated accurately. Measuring the width of the containers (calculating the surface areas may also have introduced errors by rounding to the nearest cm^2).
8. The children could have used more containers to obtain more readings for the graph. They could have placed the containers away from the window, as variations in the amount of sunlight may have affected the results.
9. The greater the surface area of the container, the faster the water evaporates (the greater the rate of evaporation). For notes on comparative statements, see page 6 in the Introduction.

THE SCIENCE BEHIND THE DATA

Materials are held together by forces of attraction between particles. Solids are held together by strong forces: the particles are held in a close, regular pattern. Liquids have weaker forces between the particles, which can move from one position to another. If the particles are moving rapidly and are near the surface of a liquid, they can escape from it (evaporation). The particles are now in a gaseous form: they are moving very rapidly and are far apart.

Only the particles at the surface of a liquid can evaporate and escape from the liquid. Doubling the surface area doubles the number of particles that can leave the liquid surface at any one time, so it should double the rate of evaporation. In the investigation described opposite, the amount of water evaporated over a week gives a relative measure of the rate of evaporation. This means that the graph of amount of water evaporated against surface area of water should be a straight line – but if you do this in a normal room, with real children, you will probably not get a straight line, and that's quite acceptable. You can use this activity to discuss the reliability of scientific data.

The children may observe bubbles forming on the inside of the container. Water contains dissolved oxygen; tiny bubbles of oxygen forming in the liquid provide new surfaces at which more dissolved oxygen can escape, causing the bubbles to grow.

Does surface area affect evaporation?

A group of children had been discussing evaporation with their teacher. They decided to investigate whether the surface area affected the rate of evaporation. They put $100cm^3$ of water into each of four containers with different cross-sectional areas, then put the containers on a warm shelf near the window and left them for a week. Then they measured the amount of water left in each container.

The children plotted a stick graph to show the surface area of the water against the amount of water that evaporated in a week.

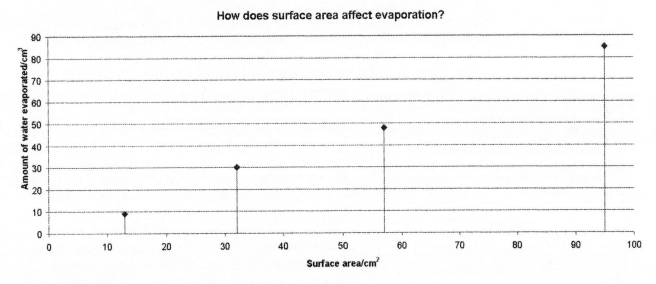

How does surface area affect evaporation?

Questions

1. Do you think a line drawn through the points on the graph should start at (0,0)?

2. Explain your answer to Question 1.

3. How much water had evaporated from the container with a surface area of $13cm^2$ in a week?

4. Complete the stick graph by drawing a line to show the trend.

5. How much water would evaporate from a surface area of $50cm^2$ in a week?

6. Why do you think the points do not make a perfect straight line?

7. What difficulties might the children have experienced in doing their investigation?

8. Describe one way in which you think the children could have improved their investigation.

9. What does the graph tell you about surface area and evaporation?

DOES WATER EVAPORATE FASTER IN WIDER BEAKERS?

> *National Curriculum Science* KS2 PoS Sc3: 2d
> *QCA Science* Unit 5D: Changing state
> *Scottish 5–14 Guidelines* Changing materials – Levels C, D

HOW TO GATHER THE DATA

This investigation can be part of a series to probe the children's ideas about evaporation. Place the beakers in an area of the classroom (such as a windowsill) where they can observe the changes. Measure the amount of water left in each beaker each day, either by its height on a marked scale or, more accurately, by using a measuring cylinder. The water lost in transfer should not affect the pattern of results. You could also pour $100cm^3$ of water into a wide container such as a plastic tank and ask the children to observe when the water has all evaporated. They can draw round the bottom of each beaker on centimetre squared paper and carefully work out the cross-sectional areas.

Answers

1. A prediction close to $65cm^3$.
2. $6cm^3$. The child should read the question carefully and subtract $94cm^3$ from $100cm^3$.
3. $17cm^3$
4. The plotted line graph should have the following shape:

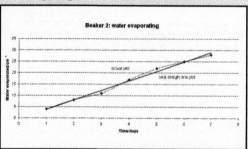

Accept either a line joining all the points or a straight line of best fit (as these are real data, they do not make a perfect straight line).
5. Almost a straight line. (Discuss with the children why errors in the investigation mean that the line is not exactly straight. Ask them to say which results should have been checked, and to predict 'correct' values for anomalous results. Modifying the data in a spreadsheet to produce a perfect straight line is an opportunity for the children to demonstrate a relatively high-level use of ICT.)
6. About the same amount of water evaporated from the beaker each day. The variations may have occurred because the beakers were left on a windowsill: slightly more water would evaporate on a sunny day than on a cloudy day.
7. Beaker 4
8. Beaker 1
9. The greater the surface area of the water, the faster the water evaporates.

THE SCIENCE BEHIND THE DATA

Reports summarising KS2 test performances (*Standards at KS2*, QCA 1996–2000) have shown that many children reaching the end of Key Stage 2 find the concepts of evaporation, condensation and dissolving difficult. They need to be given practical experiences of these processes, and encouraged to relate these to everyday life. For example, wet clothes dry out faster if they are spread out. If the children dry paper towels in the classroom, a spread-out towel will dry faster than a squeezed-up one.

Materials are held together by forces of attraction between particles. Solids are held together by strong forces: the particles are held in a close, regular pattern. Liquids have weaker forces between the particles, which can move from one position to another. If the particles are moving rapidly and are near the surface of a liquid, they can escape from it (evaporation). The particles are now in a gas: they are moving very rapidly and are far apart.

Only the particles at the surface of a liquid can evaporate and escape from the liquid. Doubling the surface area doubles the number of particles that can leave the surface at any one time, so it should double the rate of evaporation. This means that a graph of amount of water evaporated against surface area of water should be a straight line – but if you do this under normal conditions you will probably not get a straight line, and that's quite acceptable. You can use this activity to discuss the reliability of scientific data.

Does water evaporate faster in wider beakers?

Kerry, Sarah, Richard and Asif were thinking about evaporation. They had seen clothes at home spread out on the washing line, and wondered whether the area of a surface had an effect on evaporation. They set up four beakers with different cross-sectional areas, put 100cm³ of water in each and placed them next to each other on the windowsill. They measured how much water evaporated from each beaker over seven days, recording their data in a table.

Day	Amount of water evaporated/cm³			
	Beaker 1 (13cm² area)	Beaker 2 (32cm² area)	Beaker 3 (57cm² area)	Beaker 4 (95cm² area)
1	1	4	5	22
2	2	8	13	33
3	3	11		45
4	4	17	22	
5		22	30	85
6	7	25	34	98
7	8	28	40	100

Questions

1. Kerry and Asif measured the amount of water in Beaker 4 after four days. What would you predict it to be? Write your prediction in the correct place in the table.

2. Sarah and Richard measured the amount of water in Beaker 1 after five days. It was 94cm³. Write the amount of water that had evaporated in the correct place in the table.

3. Sarah and Kerry measured the amount of water in Beaker 3 after three days. It was 83cm³. Write the amount of water that had evaporated in the correct place in the table.

4. Use the results for Beaker 2 to plot a graph of the amount of water evaporated over seven days.

5. What was the shape of the graph you obtained?

6. What does this tell you about how the water evaporated?

7. Which beaker did the most water evaporate from?

8. Which beaker did the least water evaporate from?

9. What do these results tell you about evaporation and surface area?

HANDLING SCIENCE DATA YEAR 5

PUDDLES

National Curriculum Science KS2 PoS Sc3: 2b, d
QCA Science Unit 5D: Changing state
Scottish 5–14 Guidelines Changing materials – Levels C, D

HOW TO GATHER THE DATA

The children can decide whether they want to measure across the puddle or round the circumference (using a piece of string or a trundle wheel). The activity can also be 'modelled' on a board by making a circle shape with a wet (but not dripping) cloth. Some surfaces (such as cloth-type boards) work well; but with other surfaces or in warm classrooms, the evaporation can be very rapid and uneven. The children can either measure the puddle or draw round its perimeter and measure later.

THE SCIENCE BEHIND THE DATA

Materials are held together by forces of attraction between particles. Solids are held together by strong forces: the particles are held in a close, regular pattern. Liquids have weaker forces between the particles, which can move from one position to another. If the particles are moving rapidly and are near the surface of a liquid, they can escape from it (evaporation). The particles are now in a gas: they are moving very rapidly and are far apart.

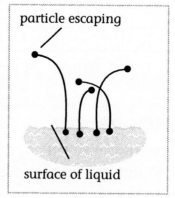

particle escaping

surface of liquid

Particles vibrate more, move faster and move further apart if energy (for example, heat) is supplied to them. As a liquid evaporates, the particles with the most energy escape from it – so the temperature of the liquid drops. A liquid will evaporate faster if the air around it is warmer, because more energy is available to make the particles move – so liquids evaporate faster in summer, when the air is warmer. However, puddles in winter will eventually dry out. If a material is in a liquid state it can evaporate, no matter what its temperature is.

In this activity, you may have to deal with some children's ideas that the water from puddles only disappears because it soaks into the ground. You can use open and closed containers in the classroom to demonstrate that water disappears from an open container when it will not disappear from a similar closed container – so the water is escaping into the air.

The lines on the graph are both curves because the rate of evaporation depends on the surface area of the puddle, which is proportional to the width squared. This means that the slope of the graph decreases with time.

Answers

1. Using a (waterproof) tape measure or a metre rule – or a trundle wheel for the circumference. Centimetres.

2. The size of both puddles decreased.

3. The summer puddle dried up faster. The child may answer that the summer puddle became smaller – this is a limited answer, because eventually the winter puddle would have reached the same size. However, this answer may be the limit of some children's ability to express their ideas. Comparing evaporation rates is difficult.

4. In summer the weather is warmer, so the temperature is higher and water will evaporate faster.

5. Evaporation is a slow process at ordinary outdoor temperatures.

6. To make the test fair.

7. Winter 60–65cm (actual result 62cm); summer 15–19cm (actual result 17cm).

8. Into the air. The child may answer that it has evaporated – so ask further: *Where is the water now?* Answers such as 'It has soaked into the ground' and 'The Sun has sucked it up' are not uncommon. If these answers are given, some further investigative activities will be needed.

Puddles

There is a place in the playground where you always get a puddle when it rains. Some children measured the size of the puddle at different times during the day.

They did this one day in the summer, and then they did the same thing in the winter to see whether there was a difference.

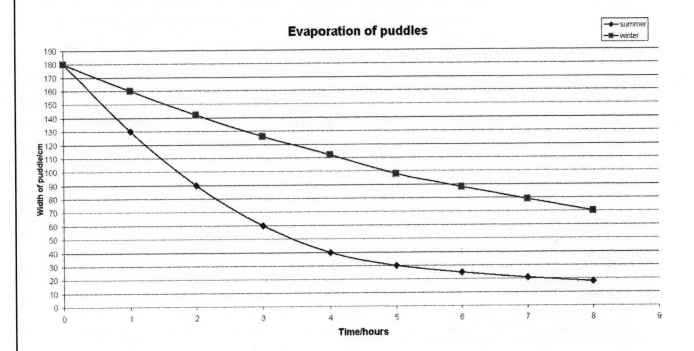

Questions

1. What do you think would be a good way to measure the size of a playground puddle? What units would you measure in?

2. What happened to the size of both puddles?

3. What is different about what happened in summer and in winter?

4. Can you explain the difference scientifically?

5. Why did it take several hours to do this puddle investigation?

6. Why did the children have to use the same place for the puddle both times?

7. Extend the two lines to predict the width of the puddles after 9 hours.

8. Where does the water from the puddles go to?

HANDLING SCIENCE DATA YEAR 5

MAKING A COLD DRINK

National Curriculum Science KS2 PoS Sc3: 2a, b, c, d
QCA Science Unit 5D: Changing state
Scottish 5–14 Guidelines Changing materials – Level C

HOW TO GATHER THE DATA

In this investigation, it is best to use a small amount of orange squash (or water) such as 30cm³ and two or three ice cubes. The fall in temperature is greater if the ratio of ice to water is higher. As in the example opposite, the whole process takes about an hour. Watch the beaker closely in order to draw the children's attention to the point when all the ice has gone.

Explore ideas about condensation with the children. Give each group a clear plastic glass or beaker with about 100cm³ of orange squash in it, and ask them to describe what the outside of the beaker feels like. They may need prompting to give the answer you want (dry). Then add about four ice cubes to each beaker and wait for about 10 minutes. Ask the children to feel the outside of the glass again. Discuss where this water comes from (condensation). If you have used orange squash, the children can taste the difference between the orange squash and the water on the outside of the glass.

THE SCIENCE BEHIND THE DATA

This investigation can be used to explore the concepts of melting and condensation, which research has shown to be difficult for children to grasp (OFSTED, 1998). After the ice is added, it takes some time for the drink to reach the minimum temperature. The water particles surrounding the ice cubes provide the energy necessary for the ice to melt. (Liquid water has more energy than ice.) As energy is taken from the water particles, the temperature of the water drops. Around 5°C, the rate at which energy flows from the water to the melting ice is equal to the rate at which it flows from the surrounding air to the water. The temperature stays the same until all the ice has melted. Then, as the water particles gain energy from their surroundings, the temperature rises back towards room temperature.

It is important to explore with the children why the temperature reaches a minimum and stays there until the ice is gone. This is not because the system is not changing (as the ice is in fact melting): it is because the rate at which energy is lost from the water to the air is equal to the rate at which it is lost from the ice to the water.

When asked Question 10, very few children give the initial response 'from the air'. You will need to use other evidence such as the colour or taste of the condensed water, or even its mass (if you have an electronic balance, you can observe an increase in mass of about 0.2g due to condensation over 30 minutes). Don't 'give' them the answer: let them use evidence to draw a logical conclusion. Believe me, one or two children will!

Answers

1. 22°C
2. Its temperature decreased (fell, dropped).
3. Most children will say that the ice was mixing with the water. However, this is not really an explanation. To 'explain' means to give reasons, using scientific knowledge and understanding. For example: the ice was colder than the water, so energy from the water particles was used to melt the ice (change it from a solid to a liquid), so the water particles had less energy and the temperature of the water went down.
4. About 4.5°C
5. About 10 minutes.
6. After about 35–40 minutes.
7. It would return to room temperature.
8. It stayed at approximately the same temperature.
9. 17.5°C (the difference between answers 1 and 4).
10. Several answers may be expected. It is important to have a discussion with the children, and to demonstrate the process if the children have not experienced it. The scientific explanation is that the outside surface of the glass becomes colder, so it condenses water vapour that is present in the air. To discuss this, it will be useful to explore what is in the air beforehand.

Making a cold drink

Joanne felt really hot, so she decided to make a cold drink. She poured about 50cm³ of orange squash and water into a plastic glass and tasted it. It wasn't cold! So she decided to add some ice cubes to the drink to make it cold. It still did not taste cold, so she decided to investigate how long it would take for the ice cubes to make her drink cold. She used a datalogger fitted with a temperature probe to measure the temperature of her drink.

This is the graph she obtained.

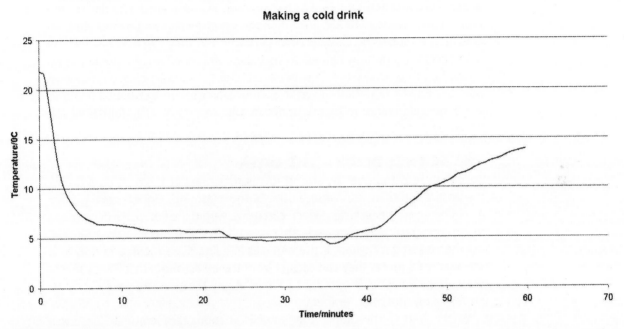

Questions

1. What was the temperature of the orange squash at the start?

2. What happened to the temperature of the orange squash in the first 2–3 minutes?

3. Can you explain why?

4. What was the lowest temperature of the orange squash?

5. How long should Joanne wait to drink her orange squash so it tastes cold?

6. When was there no longer any ice left in the orange squash?

7. What would happen to the temperature of the water if the drink were left for 120 minutes?

8. What happened to the temperature of the water between 20 and 35 minutes?

9. What was the difference in temperature between when Joanne first mixed the orange squash and when the drink was very cold?

10. Joanne noticed that the outside of her glass became cloudy and wet after she added the ice. Why do you think this happened?

HANDLING SCIENCE DATA YEAR 5

HEATING A KETTLE

National Curriculum Science KS2 PoS Sc3: 2b, c, d
QCA Science Unit 5D: Changing state
Scottish 5–14 Guidelines Changing materials – Level C

HOW TO GATHER THE DATA

This investigation is an ideal opportunity to use a datalogger. This will be safer because you, and more importantly the children, are remote from the hot water. Also, research has shown that children are able to handle data much more readily if the data are 'live', happening and changing as the children watch. They know the kettle is getting hotter and they can see that the line being plotted is getting higher, so they can relate the two. Fill the kettle no more than three-quarters full, to avoid splashing. You will need to remove or raise the lid of the kettle to keep it boiling. Don't let the kettle boil dry, and warn the children not to try this at home. Discuss why modern kettles switch off automatically.

THE SCIENCE BEHIND THE DATA

Solids are held together by strong forces (of attraction), which means that the particles in them can vibrate but not move around. Liquids have weaker forces between the particles, which can move within the liquid. Particles move much more rapidly and move further apart if energy is put into the material, as when a kettle is heated. If the particles in a liquid are moving rapidly and are near the surface, they can escape from the liquid altogether. This process is called evaporation; it occurs in a liquid at any temperature, but will occur more rapidly at higher temperatures.

At the start of the graph, the water is at room temperature. There is a slight delay in the temperature rise while the hotter water rises from the heating element towards the temperature probe. Then the temperature rises steadily, because the heating is constant. Above 90°C, the graph begins to level out because rapid evaporation is taking place and heat is escaping with the water vapour. The element is producing heat at the same rate, but the heat loss is more rapid than before. At 100°C the water is losing heat as fast as it is gaining heat, so the temperature does not rise any further. If heat were supplied faster (using a more powerful kettle), the water would simply boil more fiercely, convert more liquid to gas and lose the heat more quickly – so the temperature will stay constant.

In this activity, the children can see the 'steam' (water droplets), so they can relate this to the idea of water vapour (which is invisible) going into the air and then reappearing on a cold window-pane.

Answers

1. 20°C

2. At the start, the water was at room temperature, which was above the freezing point of water (if it were at 0°C, the water would be ice).

3. The temperature rises steadily.

4. After about 3 minutes.

5. The temperature stops rising and remains constant.

6. As the water boils it loses energy (heat) as fast as it gains energy, so the temperature does not rise. This is a difficult question but some children are capable of reasoning it out. The most common response is that the water is at boiling point (100°C) – but we want to know **why** it stays at a constant value, so an explanation in terms of energy is needed.

7. 100°C.

8. The temperature will fall.

9. 20°C

10. The water loses energy (heat) to its surroundings because it is hotter than the air around it. When it reaches room temperature, it gains heat from the room at the same rate that it loses heat to the room – so its temperature will stay the same.

Heating a kettle

A temperature sensor was placed in a kettle of water to monitor how the temperature of the water in the kettle changed after it was switched on.

This graph shows the temperatures measured.

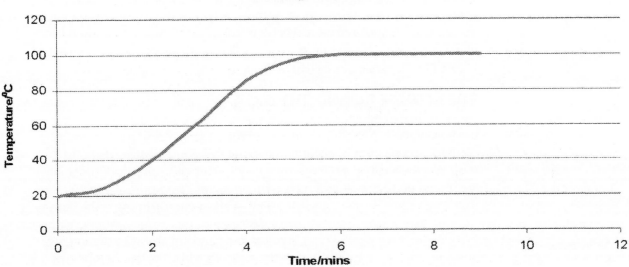

Heating a kettle

Questions

1. What is the temperature of the water at the start?

2. Why is the start temperature **not** 0°C?

3. What is happening to the temperature between 2 minutes and 4 minutes?

4. When does the temperature reach 60°C?

5. What happens to the temperature after 6 minutes?

6. Can you explain why this happens?

7. What do you think the temperature will be at 10 minutes (if the kettle is kept switched on)?

The kettle was then switched off and left for a few hours.

8. What do you think happened to the temperature of the water?

9. What do you think its temperature was after a few hours?

10. Explain your answer to Question 9.

HANDLING SCIENCE DATA YEAR 5

NOISY INSTRUMENTS

National Curriculum Science KS2 PoS Sc4 3e, f
QCA Science Unit 5F: Changing sounds
Scottish 5–14 Guidelines Science Properties and uses of energy: Level C

HOW TO GATHER THE DATA

This is a good investigation for the children to plan out, because the principle of the investigation is quite simple: to hit or shake each instrument and take a reading. The children can think of ways to achieve a fair test, and they can appreciate the value of taking an average of two or three readings for each instrument. They can predict what level of loudness will be measured for each instrument, and this develops the skill of using evidence from previous experience to refine a prediction.

THE SCIENCE BEHIND THE DATA

Sound is created by vibrations, and a sound travels from one point to another by the vibrations passing through a medium. Sound cannot pass through a vacuum (secondary schools often have suitable equipment to demonstrate this). When you strike a musical instrument, it vibrates, and these vibrations are passed on to the air around it. The vibrations cause pressure changes in the air that affect our eardrums or the sensor on a datalogger. You can feel vibrating air by putting your hand just above a vibrating ruler on the edge of a table. The loudness (volume) of a sound depends on the size (amplitude) of the vibrations. If larger vibrations are made (for example, by pulling, hitting or blowing harder), the sound will be louder. Also, our ears respond differently to different pitches of sound (high or low), so certain pitches appear louder than others. Pitch is related to the speed (frequency) of the vibrations.

Metal is a good material for producing sounds: it is described as 'sonorous' or 'ringing'. The sounds made with a metal instrument can be very clear and resonant. The instrument continues to vibrate, so the sound only dies away slowly. This property is due to the structure of metals. A large metal instrument such as a pair of cymbals makes a loud sound – but so does the triangle, which surprises some children. Wood gives a much 'deader' sound that dies away more quickly. The shape, material and size of the 'sound box' on an instrument such as a bongo drum or a traditional guitar result in complex modifications of the vibrations that affect the loudness and duration of the sound.

Answers

1. They should keep the distance from the datalogger to the instrument the same, have the same force of shake or hit (as far as possible), and keep the background noise level as low as possible.

2. They should take an average of two or three readings.

3.

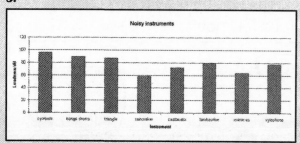

4. Cymbals

5. Sensible suggestions should refer to the cymbals being made of metal, being relatively large and being struck together.

6. Rainmaker

7. Xylophone

8. 38dB

9. Rainmaker, maracas, castanets, xylophone, tambourine, triangle, bongo drum, cymbals.

10. Look for appropriate sections of a planning sheet completed according to the child's planned investigation. Possible topics to investigate include: the effect of hitting or blowing an instrument with different amounts of force; which child can make the loudest sound with a given instrument; the loudness of various home-made instruments.

Noisy instruments

Class 5 were using a datalogger to measure the loudness of different instruments they had on their music trolley. Loudness is measured in decibels (dB).

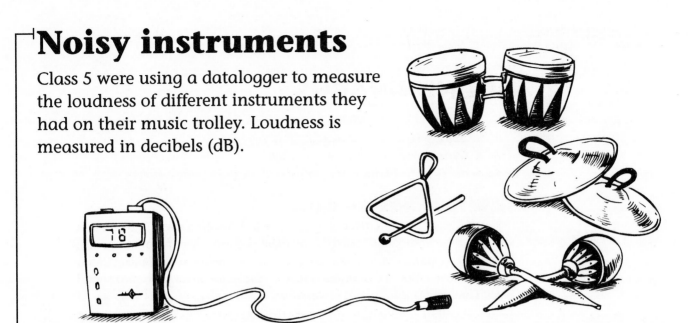

Questions

1. Describe three things the children should do to make sure their test is fair.

2. Describe one thing they should do to make sure their results are reliable.

This table shows the results of their investigation.

3. Plot a bar graph of their results on the sheet you are given.

4. Which is the loudest instrument?

5. Can you explain why it is the loudest?

6. Which is the quietest instrument?

7. Which instrument gives the decibel reading shown on the datalogger in the picture above?

8. What is the difference in decibels between the loudest instrument and the quietest?

9. Write a list of the instruments in order from the quietest to the loudest.

10. Think of another investigation that involves measuring the loudness of instruments. Write a plan for this investigation. Your plan should include:

- what you will change each time
- what you will measure each time
- what you will keep the same each time
- a blank table for your results, with headings and units
- a blank graph for your results (label the axes and give the units).

Name of instrument	Loudness/dB
cymbals	96
bongo drums	89
triangle	87
rainmaker	58
castanets	72
tambourine	80
maracas	64
xylophone	78

SOUND GRAPHS

National Curriculum Science KS2 PoS Sc4: 3e, f, g
QCA Science Unit 5F: Changing sounds
Scottish 5–14 Guidelines Properties and uses of energy – Level C

HOW TO GATHER THE DATA

This activity is a good datalogging exercise to do with a class. The children can plan the investigation together and make predictions as it proceeds, while different groups can take measurements and record the results. A keyboard or a cassette recording of a single note will give a reasonably constant sound level. There is a small amount of variation, but the children will be happy to judge the 'most frequent' or 'average' reading. They should be aware that sometimes we have to make subjective judgements in science.

Encourage the children to make predictions about the shape of the graph – for example: *Will the line go up or down?* (Do not expect them to predict a curve.) *Will it go to zero?* (Many children assume that, but this activity encourages them to think in a more focused way. *If the sound level goes to zero, that means they cannot hear it. Would that happen in a classroom? Would it happen outside?*)

THE SCIENCE BEHIND THE DATA

Sound consists of vibrations. A sound is transmitted from one point to another by the vibrations passing through a medium. Solids are better able to transmit sound than liquids, and liquids are better able than gases. With a solid medium, the sound travels faster and is heard as a louder sound. The particles in a solid are very close together, and the vibrations can pass easily between them. In a gas the particles are far apart, so it is much more difficult for them to pass on vibrations.

However, if a sound is travelling through the air and meets a solid object, some of the sound vibrations are reflected back off the surface, or pass along the solid rather than through it. This is why solid objects block sounds. Children are often surprised when they find out that sound passes through solids better than through gases, since their everyday experience tells them that sound is blocked by doors, walls and windows. However, their experience of echoes will tell them that the sound is being reflected.

A sound becomes less loud as you move away from the sound source, because the energy of the vibrations is spreading out in all directions. The loudness is inversely proportional to the square of the distance (as with light intensity), so the graph is a curve. The 'bump' in the second graph may have been caused by echoed sound. The loudness of a sound also depends on its pitch, since the human ear is more sensitive to certain frequencies (we cannot hear ultrasound at all).

Answers

1. One note gives a constant sound level, whereas the loudness of a piece of music will vary.
2. Changing the pitch may alter the reading of the sound level.
3. Next to the keyboard (zero distance).
4. Beyond 7m from the keyboard.
5. The sound is echoing from the walls, so it does not fade below a certain level as long as the sensor remains in the same room as the keyboard.
6. The greater the distance from the keyboard, the quieter the sound. (See page 6 in the Introduction, for notes on comparative statements.)
7. The result for 5m.
8. Look for a smooth curve that misses out the point given on the graph for a distance of 5m.

Sound graphs

Investigation 1

Some children were playing a note on a keyboard and measuring the loudness of the sound with a sound meter. They measured the sound level at different distances (in the same room) from the keyboard.

They plotted the results on a graph.

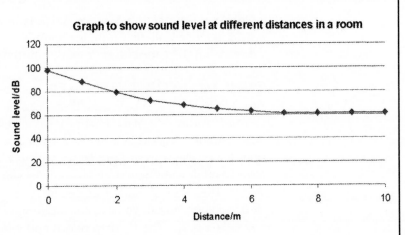

Graph to show sound level at different distances in a room

Questions

1. Why is it a good idea to measure the loudness of one note on a keyboard rather than the loudness of a piece of music?

2. Why should the children use the same note for each measurement, rather than a different note each time?

3. Where is the sound the loudest?

4. Where is the sound the quietest?

5. Why does the sound level not fall to 0dB as you move further away?

6. Describe how the sound level changes with distance from the keyboard.

Investigation 2

Some other children carried out the same investigation in a different classroom.

This graph shows their results.

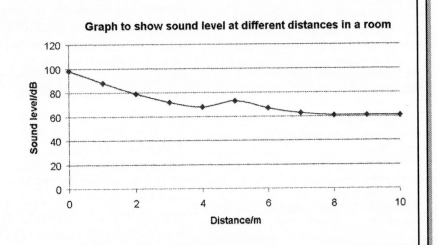

Graph to show sound level at different distances in a room

7. Which particular result do you think they should check?

8. Sketch over the top how you think the line should look.

HANDLING SCIENCE DATA YEAR 5

TRAFFIC LIGHTS

National Curriculum Science PoS Sc4: 3f
QCA Science Unit 5F: Changing sounds
Scottish 5–14 Guidelines Properties and uses of energy: Level D

HOW TO GATHER THE DATA

You will need a sound sensor that is easily portable, such as Ecolog or Explorer, and a safe place for the children to stand while they collect the data. (Explorer is available from DCP Microelectronics at dcpmicro@aol.com; Ecolog is available from Data Harvest.) It is a good idea for the children to have an adult with them in order to make sure that they do not distract any drivers. The sensor should be placed about 2m from the road, pointed at the road, and not moved. You can collect as much data as you like and interpret it at a later stage. The children might find it helpful to note down what was happening at various points. The data have been simplified for this activity, but they are real data of the kind that children can collect. Note that the data will be easier to interpret if you choose a place where there are reasonable gaps between the vehicles.

THE SCIENCE BEHIND THE DATA

Sound is produced by vibration, and sound vibrations can pass through the air to a sensor. The loudness (volume) of a sound depends on the size of the vibrations – for example, vibrations caused by a heavy lorry on the road can be heard some distance away. The pitch of a sound depends on how close the vibrations are: if an object is vibrating rapidly, it gives many vibrations in a short time and the pitch of the sound is high.

The noise made by vehicles is a combination of the engine vibrating and the tyres vibrating. As a car approaches a sensor, the sound gets louder; as it goes away, the sound gets quieter. The pitch also changes: it is higher as the car approaches and lower as the car goes away. When the car is approaching, the vehicle moves nearer in the time taken between one vibration and the next. The vibrations are closer together than those produced by a stationary vehicle, so the pitch of the sound is higher. As the car moves away, the opposite happens: the car has moved further away between one vibration and the next. The vibrations are further apart, so the pitch of the sound is lower.

These data were collected on a busy city road, so the peaks were close together (indicating frequent traffic) and the level of background noise was higher than it would be in a more rural area. It is surprising how much can be interpreted from the graph. More able children may realise that since the traffic from the minor road was quieter, the sensor must have been nearer to the major road. They might also suggest that the first car on the graph was turning away from the sensor and the second one went straight across the junction, so was louder. They could investigate the relative loudness of different vehicles.

Answers

1. The loudness of the sound increased whenever a car was passing by. (The child needs to realise this in order to answer the subsequent questions, so it is a good idea to check this answer before proceeding.)
2. Five (one for each peak).
3. At 30 seconds.
4. The sound level dropped (because no traffic was moving).
5. Two (one for each peak).
6. At 50 seconds.
7. The first set.
8. The first road is a main road, and the second is a side road with less traffic. (Accept any other sensible suggestions.)
9. The first set.
10. The loudness was much higher for the first set.
11. There is always some background noise on a street, especially during the day.

Traffic lights

Martin, Paul and Angie were using a sound sensor to measure how loud the traffic noise was near a road junction. They connected the sensor to a computer, which created this graph.

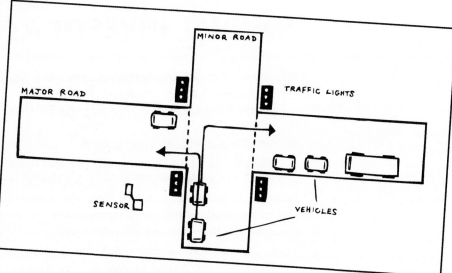

Traffic lights

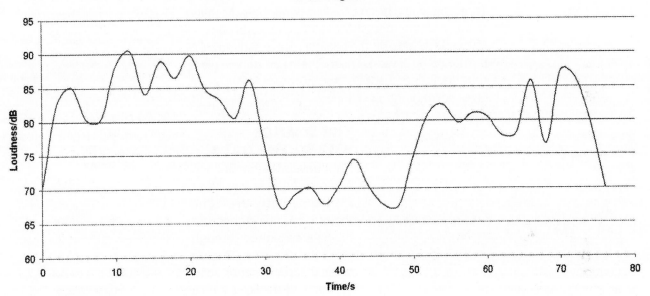

Questions

1. Why do you think the loudness of the sound went up and down?
2. How many cars went through the traffic lights in the first 30 seconds?
3. When did the traffic lights first change?
4. How can you tell this from the graph?
5. How many cars then went through the lights in the other direction?
6. When did the lights change back?
7. Which set of traffic had a longer time on green?
8. Can you think of a reason why the times on green were not the same?
9. Which set of traffic do you think the children were nearer to?
10. How can you tell this from the graph?
11. Why do you think the loudness did not go down to 0dB at any time?

HANDLING SCIENCE DATA YEAR 5

SUNDIAL INVESTIGATION

National Curriculum Science KS2 PoS Sc4: 3b, 4b, c
QCA Science Unit 5E: Earth, Sun and Moon
Scottish 5–14 Guidelines Earth in space – Level B

HOW TO GATHER THE DATA

For this activity, choose a fine sunny day and put a rounders (or similar) post at a point in the playground where it will not be disturbed. The children can draw the length of the shadow each hour with chalk, or draw a mark at the end of the shadow; then they can measure the shadow's length with a tape measure, metre rule or trundle wheel. They need to start as early as possible in the day and finish as late as possible. It would be useful to obtain a set of results at a different time of year for comparison. Remember that daylight saving time (BST) operates in summer in the UK, so the shortest shadow is at 1pm. This would be an excellent opportunity to share results with Internet partner schools in other parts of the world. Midday at the equator gives no shadow (at the right time of year). The southern hemisphere gives south-pointing shadows, the northern hemisphere gives north-pointing shadows.

Answers

1. Bar graph.
2. Line graph.
3. 1pm
4. The Sun is highest in the sky, so its angle to the stick is smallest.
5. 9am
6. The shadow becomes steadily shorter each hour from 9am to 1pm. Then it becomes longer again at the same rate.
7. The child should draw bars and points at approximately 135cm and 160cm (corresponding to the values for 10am and 9am).
8. and **9.** See diagram.

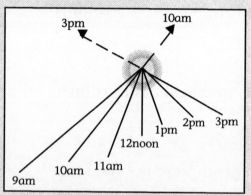

10. The rotation (spin) of the Earth causes the apparent position of the Sun in the sky to change, so that the angle of the sunlight to the stick changes. This angle is shortest at 1pm and longest at dawn and sunset.

THE SCIENCE BEHIND THE DATA

Light travels in straight lines. Any opaque object will cast a shadow with the same shape as the object, because the light cannot go through it or bend around it. The size of the shadow depends upon the angle of the light source to the object. The shadow of the sundial moves because the Earth is turning or rotating about its own axis.

This concept can be quite a difficult one for children to understand. The diagram above right (which shows a view looking down on the North Pole) can be used to help explain why the Sun appears to move across the sky. The process can also be modelled using a globe with a stick of Blu-Tack (1cm tall) stuck on it, and a light source such as an OHP. When you have set up the OHP and globe at approximately the same height (make minor adjustments to get the best effect), you can turn the globe anticlockwise and the shadow will change both in direction and in length – just as the shadow of a sundial does. Explain that the effect is produced by the rotation of the Earth while the Sun remains still (at least relative to the Solar System).

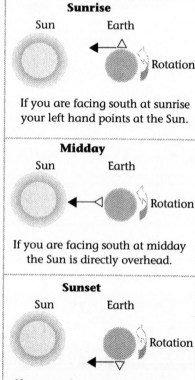

Sunrise

Sun   Earth

Rotation

If you are facing south at sunrise your left hand points at the Sun.

Midday

Sun   Earth

Rotation

If you are facing south at midday the Sun is directly overhead.

Sunset

Sun   Earth

Rotation

If you are facing south at sunset your right hand points at the Sun.

Sundial investigation

On a sunny day, some children took a rounders post into the playground to measure its shadow. They measured the shadow every hour starting at 9am and finishing at 3pm. They made two graphs from their results.

Graph A

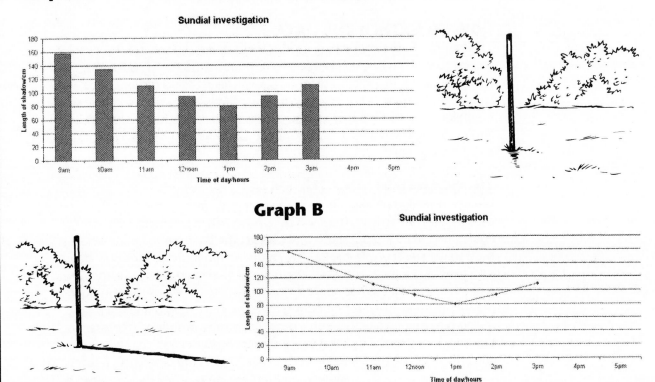

Graph B

Questions

1. What type of graph is Graph A?

2. What type of graph is Graph B?

3. When was the shadow the shortest?

4. Why do you think the shadow was the shortest then?

5. When was the shadow the longest?

6. Describe what happens to the length of the shadow during the day from 9am to 3pm.

7. On both graphs, show how long you would expect the shadow to be at 4pm and 5pm.

8. Draw a 'bird's eye view' diagram to show the positions of all the shadows on the ground.

9. For the shadows at 10am and 3pm, draw arrows on the same diagram to show the direction of the Sun.

10. Use what you know about the Sun and the Earth to explain why the shadow changes during the day.

SUNRISE, SUNSET

National Curriculum Science KS2 PoS Sc4 4b, c, d
QCA Science Unit 5E: Earth, Sun and Moon
Scottish 5–14 Guidelines Science Earth in space: Level E

HOW TO GATHER THE DATA

Children can find data relating to the times of sunset and sunrise in their nearest town from bbc.co.uk/weather, or from the US Naval Astronomy site (www.usno.navy.mil/science.shtml). They will need to find the longitude and latitude of the town (from www.astro.com/cgi/atlw3/aq.cgi) first. Make sure the children understand that 24-hour clock times are not the same as decimal figures: the minutes after the **:** symbol go up to 59, not 99, before making an additional hour.

THE SCIENCE BEHIND THE DATA

Discuss the children's experience of the changing times of sunrise and sunset before doing this activity. The Earth spins on its axis in one mean solar day (24 hours), and the Sun appears to move across the sky from the east (where it rises) to the west (where it sets). The Earth also orbits around the Sun in one solar year (365 days, 5 hours, 48 minutes and 46 seconds). Because the Earth is tilted on its axis, the northern hemisphere is tilted towards the Sun during the summer and away from it during the winter (see diagram below).

You can demonstrate this with a large globe and a desk lamp (representing the Sun). Show the children that the Earth spins on its axis anti-clockwise, so the Sun only shines on the UK for part of the day. Discuss the differences between summer and winter. Demonstrate that because the Earth is tilted on its axis, there are more hours of daylight in the UK in summer than in winter. Ask the children what they have noticed about the position of the Sun in the sky at various times of the year. The Sun makes a lower arc (casting longer shadows) in winter than summer.

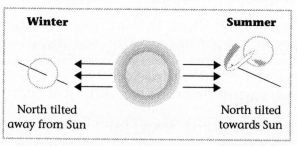

Winter	Summer
North tilted away from Sun	North tilted towards Sun

This topic provides good cross-curricular links to geography. Can any of the children explain why we put the clocks forward between April and October? The reason is to help us make better use of the daylight in the summer. This is important for people working outdoors and travelling to and from work or school.

Answers

1. January, December.
2. At 4pm in December and 4.30pm in January.
3. 8½ hours (December), 8 hours (January).
4. It would be getting dark.
5. June
6. 8.21pm (20:21 hours)
7. Approximately 16½ hours.
8. Midsummer's Day – because it is the longest day of the year.
9. The time of sunrise gets steadily earlier. Look for interpretation of the graph: responses such as 'The bars get shorter' are describing the graph, but not interpreting the data.
10. The time of sunrise gets steadily later. Again, look for interpretation of the graph.
11. In Britain, the clocks are adjusted: they are moved one hour forward in late March, then moved back in late October – so the sunrise and sunset times from April to October are an hour ahead of those in the table.
12. In the summer the northern part of the Earth tilts towards the Sun, so the Sun appears higher in the sky above London and there are more daylight hours. In the winter the northern part of the Earth tilts away from the Sun, so the Sun appears lower in the sky above London and there are fewer daylight hours.

Sunrise, sunset

A group of primary school children in London decided to use the Internet to investigate the times at which the Sun rises and sets throughout the year. They found out the sunrise and sunset times in London for the 21st day of each month in the year. They converted the times into 24-hour clock times to make the calculations easier, then plotted the graphs using a computer.

Month	Time of sunrise	Time of sunset
Jan	7.53am	4.30pm (16:30)
Feb	7.02am	5.26pm (17:26)
Mar	6.01am	6.15pm (18:15)
Apr	4.52am	7.07pm (19:07)
May	4.00am	7.54pm (19:54)
Jun	3.43am	8.21pm (20:21)
July	4.08am	8.04pm (20:04)
Aug	4.55am	7.10pm (19:10)
Sep	5.44am	6.01pm (18:01)
Oct	6.34am	4.54pm (16:54)
Nov	7.28am	4.03pm (16:03)
Dec	8.03am	3.53pm (15:53)

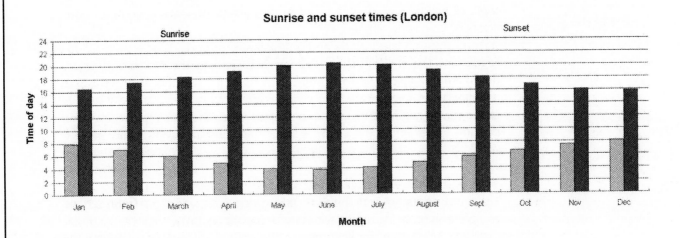

Questions

1. In which two months does the Sun rise at approximately 8am?

2. At what time does the Sun set in those months?

3. How many hours of daylight are there on the 21st day in those months?

4. If you were walking home from school at half past three in those months, would it be light, dark or getting dark?

5. In which month does the Sun rise at the earliest time?

6. At what time does the Sun set in that month?

7. How many hours of daylight are there on the 21st day of that month?

8. Find out what people call that day. Why do you think this is?

9. What happens to the time of sunrise between January and June?

10. What happens to the time of sunrise between June and December?

11. If you time the sunrises and sunsets from April to October on a clock in London, the times are not the same as the ones given in the chart. Can you explain why? (Think about what we do to the clocks in spring and autumn.)

12. Why are there only a few hours of daylight in London in the winter and many hours of daylight in the summer?

HANDLING SCIENCE DATA YEAR 5

TIME ZONES

National Curriculum Science KS2 PoS Sc4: 4c
QCA Science Unit 5E: Earth, Sun and Moon
Scottish 5–14 Guidelines Science Earth in space: Level E

HOW TO GATHER THE DATA

Time zone data can be obtained from most encyclopaedias. Encouraging the children to find out the information for themselves links with 'referencing information' in the National Literacy Strategy. A chart like the one shown opposite could be made by individuals, groups or the whole class. This activity has strong links to geography, and would contribute to display work on the topic of holidays. As people travel further afield, they are becoming more aware of time zone differences.

You can use a large globe and a desk lamp to model the Earth and Sun. First, show the children the imaginary axis (joining the North and South poles) around which the Earth spins. Now demonstrate that the Earth spins anti-clockwise. Point out where various cities are on the globe and ask the children whether it will be light or dark there when the globe is in a particular position. For example, if the light is shining on London, will it be light in New York?

THE SCIENCE BEHIND THE DATA

The Earth orbits around the Sun, taking one solar year (see page 52) to complete an orbit. The Earth also spins or rotates on its own axis in one mean solar day. Make sure the children use the correct vocabulary to distinguish between these two movements. As the Earth spins, the Sun appears to move across the sky from the east to the west (see the diagram on page 50 showing the Earth and the Sun at sunrise, midday and sunset).

The position of any place on the Earth is determined by two measurements: latitude and longitude. Latitude measures how far a place is north or south of the Equator. The Equator represents 0° latitude and the Poles represent 90°N (the North Pole) and 90°S (the South Pole). Longitude measures how far a place is east or west of the prime meridian (0° longitude), a line that runs from the North Pole to the South Pole through the Royal Astronomical Observatory at Greenwich.

The line of longitude 180°W is the same as 180°E (called the International Date Line). If you travel from east to west across this line in the Pacific, you 'lose' a whole day. 15° of longitude represents one hour of time as the Earth rotates. If you travel east of Greenwich, you must advance your clock by one hour for every 15° of longitude. At 180° east, the time is 12 hours ahead of Greenwich. Likewise, at 180° west, the time is 12 hours behind Greenwich. Therefore the time difference between two points on either side of the International Date Line is 24 hours.

Answers

1. 2pm (2 o'clock in the afternoon)
2. East
3. Tokyo
4. a) 1pm **b)** 10am
5. 7am (7 o'clock in the morning)
6. 4am
7. When the Sun starts to rise in New York (7am), it is still dark in San Francisco. If the time were not set differently, people in San Francisco would be going to school or to work in the dark.
8. West
9. Anti-clockwise. (A suitable diagram.)
10. Sydney. (This is often featured in news programmes on New Year's Eve.)

Time zones

A group of children were discussing the places they had been to on holiday. Jill had been to Disney World in Florida – she had to turn her watch back five hours, because the time in Florida was five hours behind the time in the UK. Jim had been to Egypt and had seen the pyramids – he had to move his watch forward two hours, as the time in Cairo was two hours ahead of our time. The children went on to investigate the times in other cities around the world.

This graph shows what they found out. The negative times (such as –4 hours) indicate a time behind the London time; the positive times indicate a time ahead of the London time.

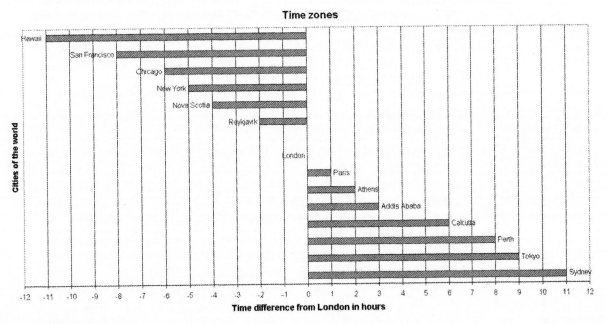

Time zones

Questions

1. If it is 12 noon (midday) in London, what time is it in Athens?

2. Is Tokyo east or west of London?

3. Does the Sun rise first in Tokyo or in London?

4. If it is 3pm in Addis Ababa, what time is it in **a)** Paris? **b)** Reykjavik?

5. If it is 12 noon in London, what time is it in New York?

6. If it is 7am in New York, what time is it in San Francisco?

7. Britain is a small country, so we are all in the same time zone. The United States is a large country. Why is it sensible for the time in San Francisco to be three hours behind the time in New York?

8. Are New York and San Francisco east or west of London?

9. Which way does the Earth spin on its axis: clockwise or anti-clockwise? Draw a diagram to show this.

10. Which city of those in the graph celebrate New Year's Day the earliest?

HANDLING SCIENCE DATA YEAR 5

PLANET DATA

National Curriculum Science KS2 PoS Sc4: 4a
QCA Science Unit 5E: Earth, Sun and Moon
Scottish 5–14 Guidelines Science Earth in space: Level C

HOW TO GATHER THE DATA

Finding data about the planets is a good opportunity for children to use CD-ROMs and Internet searches. Different groups can research different planets or different aspects of the planets (such as moons, rings, atmosphere or planet surface). The children do not need to know a lot of factual information about the planets (see below), but a topic on 'Space' invariably arouses their interest and can be used to develop their presentation skills. Work on the Earth in space provides links to other curriculum areas, such as ICT (searches, data handling), art (display work) and technology (making rockets and Moon buggies).

THE SCIENCE BEHIND THE DATA

Children only need to know about the Earth, Sun and Moon for the purposes of the English National Curriculum; however, the Scottish and Welsh curricula require them to know about wider aspects of the Solar System, such as the nine planets. Children may think of our Moon as the only one, and not realise that other planets have their own moons. A moon is any large-sized natural satellite in orbit around a planet.

There are several theories about how our Moon was formed. One is that it was 'thrown out' from the Earth. Another is that it came from outside the Solar System, but was 'captured' by the Earth as it moved through space. This is another area of science where the 'right answer' is not known, but competing theories are based on the available evidence.

■ The 'from the Earth' theory is supported by the similarity between Moon rock and some rocks in the surface of the Earth, and by the fact that the Pacific basin represents a great cavity in the Earth's surface. However, it is not easy to explain with this theory how the Moon became spherical or moved to where it is.

■ A problem for the 'gravitational attraction' theory is that the two planets nearest to the Sun do not have any moons – but they both have a higher gravitational attraction than Mars, which has two moons. It may be that the Sun's gravitational attraction has pulled the moons of Mercury and Venus out of their orbit – if they ever existed! As the number of moons seems to increase with planetary size and distance from the Sun, it may be that planets are best able to 'capture' moons if they are both large and relatively far from the Sun.

Answers

1. Pluto
2. One
3. Mercury and Venus.
4. Jupiter
5. Pluto
6. Yes
7. Accept any sensible statement, such as: The four largest planets all have more moons than the five smallest planets.
8. $1 + 2 + 17 + 18 + 15 + 8 + 1 = 62$
9. Pluto, Mercury, Mars, Venus, Earth, Neptune, Uranus, Saturn, Jupiter.
10. Allow any sensible interpretations of the data, such as:

■ There are two distinct groups: smaller planets and larger planets.

■ All of the smaller planets except Pluto are nearer to the Sun than the larger planets.

■ The number of moons a planet has generally increases with the size of the planet.

■ The number of moons a planet has increases with the planet's distance from the Sun up to Jupiter, then decreases again.

Planet data

Henry and Matt looked on the Internet to find some data about the planets. They found out the sizes of the planets and the number of moons that each planet has.

Henry and Matt plotted the data as a bar graph.

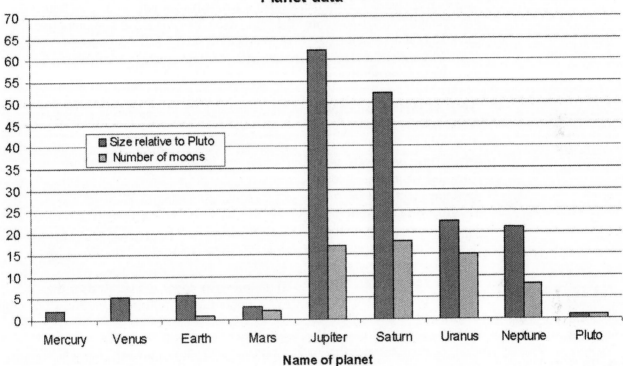

Planet data

Questions

1. Which planet has the same number of moons as the Earth?

2. How many moons does this planet have?

3. Which two planets have no moons?

4. Which is the largest planet?

5. Which is the smallest planet?

6. Does the size of the planet seem to affect how many moons it has?

7. Give reasons for your answer to Question 6.

8. What is the total number of moons in the Solar System?

9. Write a list of the planets in order of size, from the smallest to the largest.

10. Describe any patterns that you can see in the planet data.

NIGHT AND DAY

National Curriculum Science KS2 PoS Sc4: 4c, d
QCA Science Unit 5E: Earth, Sun and Moon
Scottish 5–14 Guidelines Earth in space – Level B; Properties and uses of energy – Level B

HOW TO GATHER THE DATA

This investigation was carried out in a conservatory, but it could be done anywhere suitable in the school. It is an example of the dual use of a datalogger, leading to the presentation of two different sets of data on the same graph. Set the datalogger to sense light and temperature and to run for 24 hours, and then just leave it. Some dataloggers will run on a 'remote' setting, without being connected to a computer; the data can be downloaded to the computer later. You can look at the data in graphical form on the datalogger screen, or you can transfer the data to a spreadsheet program (such as *Microsoft Excel*) in order to print out the graph.

THE SCIENCE BEHIND THE DATA

The light level will be zero when it is completely dark. This idea helps the children to understand that darkness is only the absence of light. Some children think that darkness is a physical entity that can have an effect: the shadows cover the light or take it away. The graph demonstrates that darkness means a very low light level, not a high 'dark' level.

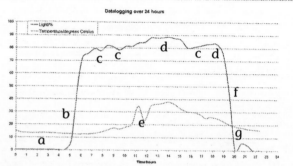

a) darkness **b)** dawn **c)** cloudy **d)** sunny
e) door opening **f)** nightfall **g)** light switched on

In the morning, as the Sun rises, the light level increases rapidly before the temperature rises. The energy from the Sun will heat things up gradually after sunrise: the particles of various objects (and the gas particles in the atmosphere) absorb energy, which makes them vibrate faster. The increased rate of vibration causes liquids to expand, so the mercury level in a thermometer will rise. During the daylight hours, the light level and temperature remain relatively high as long as the Sun shines. If the sky clouds over, the light level may change rapidly, but the temperature will take longer to alter. Changes in the level of natural light are often disguised in cities by the high level of ambient light from streetlamps, traffic and buildings, reflected from the undersides of clouds. The natural changes in light and temperature during the day and night can be modelled using a desk lamp and a globe with light and temperature sensors stuck on.

The activity also demonstrates the change in room temperature caused by opening a door to the outside, allowing hot air to escape; and the effect of a distant electric light on the level of ambient light in a room. Indoor environments may contain many such factors.

Answers

1. About 05:30 or 06:00 hrs (5.30 or 6.00am).
2. a) Either point marked d on the graph above. **b)** Any point marked c on the graph above.
3. The temperature has risen (probably due to clouds clearing while the Sun is high in the sky). The temperature line drops very quickly, then goes back up again (because there is still direct sunlight).
4. 88%
5. About 20:00 (8pm).
6. 14.5 hours
7. Someone put a light on in the house.
8. 38°C at about 14:00 (2pm).
9. If the same investigation were carried out in winter, there would be fewer hours of daylight and the temperature would be lower. This is because the northern hemisphere of the Earth is tilted towards the Sun in summer and away from the Sun in winter.

Night and day

A datalogger was used to measure the light level and temperature in a conservatory. The conservatory was attached to the back of the house. This graph shows what was recorded.

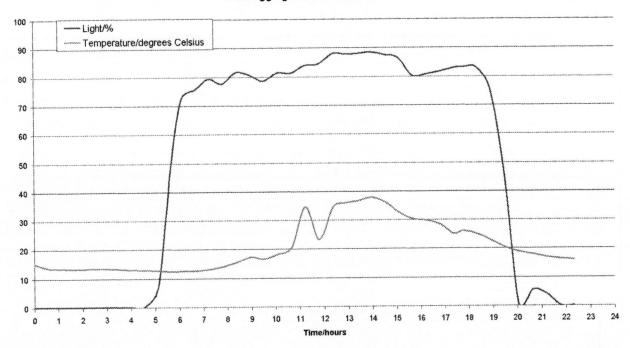

Datalogging over 24 hours

Legend:
— Light/%
··· Temperature/degrees Celsius

(x-axis: Time/hours, 0–24; y-axis: 0–100)

Questions

1. At what time do you think the Sun began to rise?

2. Sometimes it was sunny and sometimes it was cloudy. Mark two points on the graph to show **a)** a sunny time and **b)** a cloudy time.

3. Just after 11 o'clock, somebody opened the conservatory door because it was getting very hot inside. How can you tell this from the graph?

4. What was the highest light level reached all day?

5. At what time did it become completely dark?

6. How many hours of daylight were there?

7. Can you think of a reason why the light level increased slightly at about 21:00 (9pm)?

8. What was the highest temperature reached? What time was this?

9. This investigation was done in the summer. Describe two ways in which the results might be different if it were done in winter. Explain why they would be different.

Our planning board

Our question is: _____

_____

Our prediction is: _____

_____

We will change:

We will measure:

We will keep these things the same:

Our table

We will change:	We will measure:

Our graph

We will measure:

We will change:

Graph axes

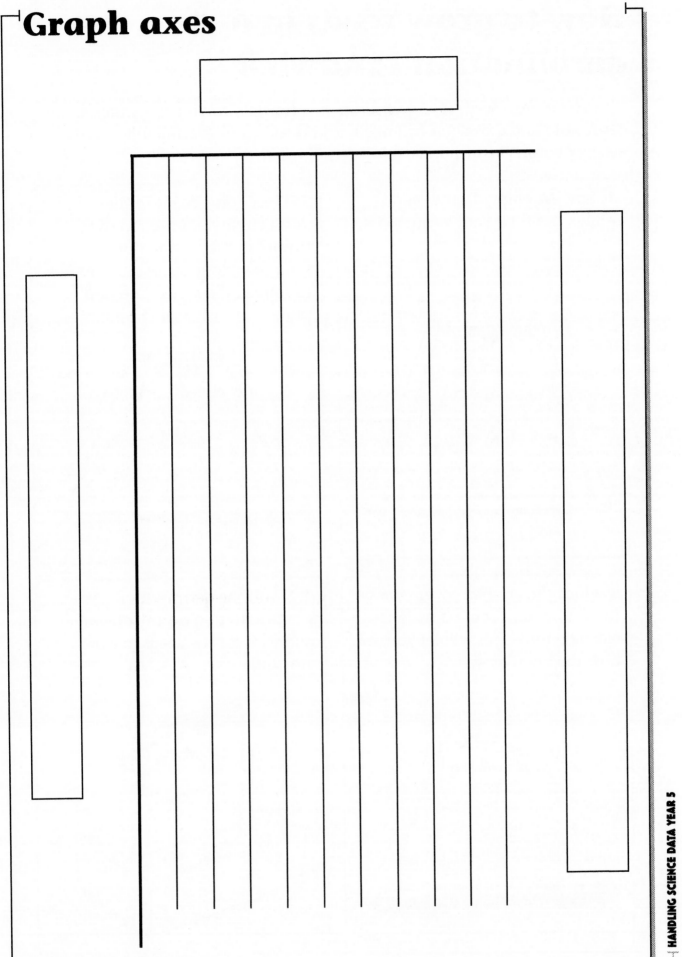

How to grow seeds in a germination sandwich

It's easy to grow seeds in a germination sandwich, so you can watch them germinate and grow. You will need: a wooden frame, vermiculite, seeds, a Perspex cover, elastic bands, a bucket of water.

1. Lay the empty frame on a table, and fill it with vermiculite.

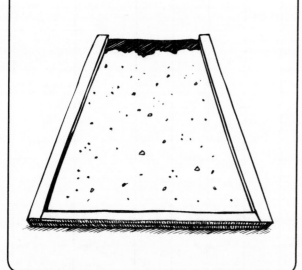

2. Place some seeds in the vermiculite near the top of the frame, so they have room for their roots to grow. Be careful not to squash the seeds, and don't put too many in the frame.

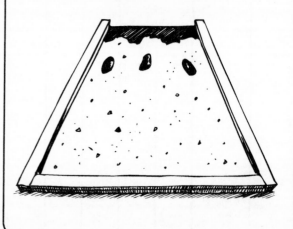

3. Place the Perspex cover over the frame and secure it with elastic bands. This will let you see how the seeds grow.

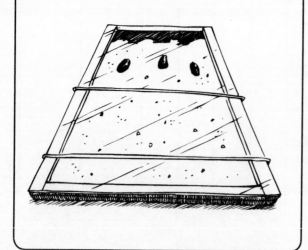

4. Stand the germination sandwich up in a tank of water, and wait for the seeds to start growing.

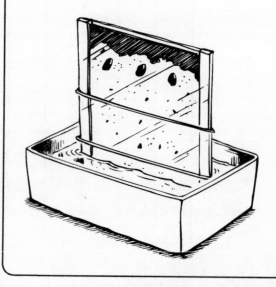